EDINBURGH GEOLOGY

EDINBURGH GEOLOGICAL SOCIETY

EDINBURGH GEOLOGY

AN EXCURSION GUIDE

Edited by

G. H. Mitchell   E. K. Walton
Douglas Grant

OLIVER AND BOYD
EDINBURGH AND LONDON

OLIVER AND BOYD

Tweeddale Court
Edinburgh 1

39A Welbeck Street
London W.1

First published 1960

Printed in Great Britain for Oliver & Boyd Ltd., Edinburgh
by Robert MacLehose & Co. Ltd., The University Press, Glasgow

CONTENTS

LIST OF PLATES

The photograph of Eildon Hills is reproduced from *The Scotsman*, the remainder by permission of the Director of H.M. Geological Survey and the Controller of H.M. Stationery Office.

LIST OF PLATES

GLOSSARY

Agglomerate.	A coarse-grained, fragmental rock with angular blocks usually set in a fine-grained matrix: results from explosive volcanic activity.
Albitization.	The process by which plagioclase feldspars in igneous rocks are enriched in soda.
Amygdale.	A vesicle or vapour cavity in an igneous rock filled with secondary minerals.
Andesite.	A volcanic rock composed essentially of plagioclase (andesine or oligoclase) and a ferro-magnesian mineral.
Banakite.	A variety of dolerite containing orthoclase in the groundmass.
Basalt.	A fine-grained igneous rock occurring as a lava or minor intrusion; composed of plagioclase (generally labradorite) and augite and sometimes olivine.
Basanite.	A basaltic rock with felspathoids (nepheline, analcite or leucite) in addition to plagioclase, augite and olivine.
Breccia.	A coarse-grained sedimentary rock with angular fragments set in a finer-grained matrix. Fault-breccias, crush-breccias and volcanic breccias also occur.
Cementstone.	A fine-grained, earthy limestone.
Corrom.	A dry delta formed on a watershed between two large valleys by a lateral stream which thereby has the chance of flowing into either one drainage basin or the other.
Crag and tail.	The form taken by a hill where a steep-sided crag of resistant rock has protected a gently sloping 'tail' of softer rock on the lee-side, from ice-erosion.

Craiglockhart basalt.	A basalt with conspicuous crystals of olivine and augite.
Dalmeny basalt.	A basalt containing abundant small phenocrysts of olivine, with augite and plagioclase generally restricted to the base.
Dolerite.	An igneous rock forming a minor intrusion and consisting of plagioclase (usually labradorite), augite and sometimes olivine: coarser in grain than basalt, and commonly with ophitic texture.
Drumlin.	An elongated, stream-lined hill of boulder-clay with its long axis in the direction of ice-flow.
Dunsapie basalt.	A basalt with large phenocrysts of labradorite, augite and olivine.
Dyke.	A wall-like intrusion of igneous rock: occasionally applied to sedimentary rocks filling fissures in previously consolidated rocks.
Felsite.	A fine-grained, generally light-coloured igneous rock usually with quartz and orthoclase.
Fluxion-structure.	A banded structure in igneous rocks formed by movement during intrusion.
Ganister.	A highly siliceous sandstone with quartz as cement; having a very fine and even granular texture; usually contains carbonaceous streaks and patches representing casts or impressions of rootlets.
Gossan.	The oxidized upper portion of a mineral vein or lode of sulphide minerals.
Greywacke.	A sandstone of mixed composition and mixed grain-size. Larger components are quartz, feldspar and rock-fragments set in a clay-cement.
Hade.	The angle between the plane of a fault and the vertical.
Hillhouse basalt.	A basalt with small phenocrysts of olivine and sometimes augite, set in a groundmass mostly of augite.
Isocline.	A fold with both limbs dipping in the same direction at approximately the same angle.
Kame.	A mound of gravel or sand formed by deposition from a stream emerging from a glacier.
Kettle-hole.	A hollow in boulder-clay or moraine caused by the

melting of a mass of ice separated from the main glacier or ice sheet.

Knick-point. The point of slope-change in the longitudinal profile of a valley, related to changes in base-level (sea-level).

Kulaite. A variety of dolerite containing the minerals nepheline, leucite and hornblende.

Laccolith or Laccolite. An igneous intrusion shaped like a mushroom without the stalk visible.

Macroporphyritic. The texture of an igneous rock where large crystals (phenocrysts) are set in a finer-grained matrix or groundmass. A diameter of 2 mm. is often taken as the limit between macro- and microporphyritic texture.

Mamelon. A rounded volcanic hill.

Markle basalt. A basalt with large crystals of labradorite and small crystals of olivine.

Micropegmatite. Aggregates of fine-grained quartz and felspar occurring as a groundmass in igneous rocks.

Microporphyritic. As in macroporphyritic. Phenocrysts (less than 2 mm.) set in a finer-grained groundmass.

Moraine. Rock debris transported by a glacier which, on the melting of the ice is deposited in front of (terminal) on the side of (lateral) or, when two glaciers coalesce, along the junction of the two (median). Similar deposits formed beneath the glacier are sometimes called ground moraine.

Mugearite. A lava, like basalt, but with the plagioclase as oligoclase rather than labradorite.

Ophitic. The texture of an igneous rock resulting from the intergrowth of plagioclase and augite whereby the former penetrate the latter. Typical of dolerite.

Orthophyric. A rock texture in which abundant stumpy rectangular sections of feldspar appear in the groundmass.

Phenocrysts. The large crystals in a porphyritic rock.

Phonolite. A fine-grained igneous rock consisting essentially of nepheline and sanidine feldspar. Rings when hammered, hence the name.

Phyric.	Porphyritic.
Porphyry.	An igneous rock with conspicuous phenocrysts set in a fine-grained matrix. Hence porphyritic.
Pyroclasts.	Fragmental deposits of volcanic ejectamenta. Hence pyroclastic.
Radiolarian chert.	A very fine-grained siliceous sedimentary rock containing remains of radiolaria.
Rhyolite.	A volcanic rock rich in silica, often showing quartz or orthoclase phenocrysts in a glassy or very finely crystalline groundmass.
Roches-moutonnees.	Elongated, smoothed and striated rock masses owing their shape to ice abrasion. Name derived from resemblance of shape to sheep-skin wigs.
Seatclay.	A clay, usually full of fossilized roots of plants, which at one time formed the soil in which the vegetation grew. Often forms the floor of a coal seam.
Sill.	A sheet of igneous rock intruded along the bedding planes of earlier rocks.
Slickensides.	The grooves or scratches formed on a fault plane as a result of the movement of adjacent rock.
Spilite.	A basaltic rock the plagioclase of which has been albitized to oligoclase or albite.
Tachylite.	A black, compact, glassy basaltic rock generally forming the chilled margin of an intrusion.
Teschenite.	A variety of dolerite characterized by the presence of analcite and soda-rich ferro-magnesian minerals.
Trachyandesite.	An igneous rock intermediate in composition between trachyte and andesite.
Trachyte.	A volcanic rock, usually porphyritic with orthoclase and ferro-magnesian minerals (biotite and augite).
Trachytoid.	A rock texture in which the crystals are arranged in a parallel or sub-parallel manner.
Tuff.	A rock composed of comparatively fine-grained volcanic ejectamenta.
Unconformity.	A break in the geological record, generally revealed by the presence of two groups of strata, the

higher of which has a different dip and strike from the lower.

Vesicles.
Cavities in igneous rocks formed by the escape of gas during consolidation.

Wash-out.
A channel cut in deposits shortly after their formation and subsequently filled by later deposits.

White trap.
An intrusive igneous rock which has been bleached and altered to white carbonate and clay minerals by contact with coal or other carbonaceous strata.

Xenolith.
A fragment or block of rock included in an igneous mass. The included material is foreign to the host.

Wrench fault.
A fault where the movement was horizontal.

Young.
A term used in structural geology to indicate the stratigraphical relationship of rocks. A bed is said to 'young' in the direction of its later-formed part regardless of whether it is at present the right way up or inverted.

MINERALS

Analcite.	Hydrated alumino-silicate of sodium.
Anglesite.	Lead sulphate.
Anhydrite.	Calcium sulphate.
Ankerite.	Mixed carbonate of iron, manganese and magnesium.
Apophyllite.	Hydrated silicate of calcium with potassium and fluorine.
Augite.	Alumino-silicate or calcium, magnesium and iron.
Barite (barytes).	Barium sulphate.
Barkevikite.	A variety of hornblende.
Biotite.	A coloured mica. An alumino-silicate of potassium and iron and magnesium.
Calcite.	Calcium carbonate.
Cerussite.	Lead carbonate.
Chalcopyrite.	Sulphide of copper and iron.
Chrysocolla.	Hydrated silicate of copper.
Chlorophaeite.	Hydrated silicate of calcium, iron and magnesium.
Cobaltite.	Sulphide of cobalt and arsenic.
Datolite.	Silicate of calcium and boron.
Galena.	Lead sulphide.
Hemimorphite.	Hydrated silicate of zinc.
Hornblende.	Alumino-silicate with calcium, sodium and potassium and iron and magnesium.
Hydrozincite.	Hydroxide and carbonate of zinc.
Jasper.	Very finely crystalline silica.
Leadhillite.	Hydrated sulphate-carbonate of lead.
Linarite.	Hydrated silicate of lead and copper.
Malachite.	Hydroxide and carbonate of copper.
Marcassite.	Iron disulphide.
Muscovite.	White mica, alumino-silicate of potassium.
Natrolite.	hydrated alumino-silicate of sodium.

Niccolite.	Nickel arsenide.
Orthoclase (feldspar).	Alumino-silicate of potassium.
Olivine.	Silicate of iron and magnesium.
Pectolite.	Silicate of sodium and calcium (with hydroxyl).
Prehnite.	Alumino-silicate of calcium (with hydroxyl).
Plagioclase (feldspar).	A series of minerals: alumino-silicates of sodium (albite, $NaAlSiO$) with increasing proportion of calcium through oligoclase-andesine-labradorite, bytownite to anorthite ($CaAlSiO$).
Pyrite.	Iron disulphide.
Pyromorphite.	Chloride-phosphate-arsenate of lead.
Quartz.	Silicon dioxide.
Rammelsbergite.	Nickel diarsenide.
Sanidine.	A variety of orthoclase feldspar.
Selenite.	Hydrated calcium sulphate (gypsum) in the form of large clear crystals.
Silica.	Oxide of silicon.
Sphalerite.	See zinc blende.
Stilpnomelane.	Silicate of iron, aluminium, and potassium sometimes with magnesium or manganese.
Smithsonite.	Zinc carbonate.
Zinc blende.	Zinc sulphide.

INTRODUCTION

The Geological Setting

The long ridge of the Pentland, Braid and Blackford hills, formed of Old Red Sandstone lavas and sediments with a Silurian core, sweeps up from the south-west straight into the centre of Edinburgh and forms, as it were, a promontory of craggy upland, around the northern end of which beats the tide of human dwellings in the suburbs of Liberton, Newington, Greenbank and Colinton. A mile to the north of Blackford Hill, Arthur's Seat, with its Lower Carboniferous volcanic rocks, rises like an island out of the sea of houses which has almost engulfed the Craiglockhart Hills, the Castle Rock and Calton Hill, formed of similar rocks, and entirely submerged the Royal Mile and the other gentler swells of ground, composed of Lower Carboniferous sediments and intrusions.

To the east between the Pentland Hills and the escarpment of the Moorfoot and Lammermuir hills lies the basin of the combined North and South Esk rivers, draining Carboniferous rocks which include the coals of the important Midlothian Coalfield. A low anticlinal ridge of limestone country, often called the Cousland ridge and in the core of which are situated gas and oil bores tapping the resources of the Lower Carboniferous, divides the Midlothian from the smaller East Lothian Coalfield in which only the Limestone Coal Group coals are developed to any extent. The lowest Carboniferous rocks appear at the surface still farther east, towards North Berwick and Dunbar. They include the many lava flows and tuffs with their associated volcanic necks and intrusions which form the Garleton Hills, the striking laws of Traprain, the

B

Bass Rock and North Berwick and much fine coast scenery near the latter place. Near Dunbar they give place to the red sandstones and conglomerates of the Old Red Sandstone, well-displayed also on the coast near Cove and Siccar Point, with an intervening development of Carboniferous Limestone near Barness.

On a fine day from Arthur's Seat or Blackford Hill or any of the higher ground of the Mid or East Lothian plains, a prominent escarpment is to be seen in the south-east. This is the line of the Southern Upland Fault which traverses Scotland from near Dunbar to Girvan and to the south of which rise the Southern Uplands, that great expanse of generally grass-covered hills, the glory of which is recorded in no uncertain manner by the imposing statue of a Scotch Blackface ram in the High Street at Moffat.

To the west of Edinburgh a rolling belt of lower ground extends through Corstorphine, Queensferry, Broxburn and Ratho to Linlithgow in the north and Cobbinshaw in the south. This is the country of the West Lothian Oil-Shale Field, much exploited in the past, as the conspicuous 'bings' of spent shale bear witness, often rising as they do to a height of a hundred feet or more above the surrounding countryside. Together with the numerous dolerite sills and dykes they form the most prominent features of the landscape. The surface as a whole is planed, grooved and so plastered with glacial drift that exposures of solid rock are few and far between except along the coast from Cramond to Blackness.

Though folded considerably, the Oil-Shales in general dip westwards and pass beneath the Bathgate lavas, of mid-Carboniferous age, which form a ridge of higher and often craggy ground extending south from Linlithgow. These rocks in turn pass westwards under the Upper Carboniferous of the Lanarkshire Coalfield with its accompanying industrial sprawl.

Across the Firth of Forth the Fife Coast comes within the

Edinburgh area and presents magnificent sections of Car-
boniferous sediments, igneous rocks and associated intrusions.
Some of the latter form striking features like the Binn of
Burntisland while the Lower Carboniferous lavas of the
Burntisland dome give rise to ground with higher relief than
that of the coalfield behind Kirkcaldy, Dysart and Leven.

The deposits of the Great Ice Age lie plentifully scattered
over the whole district, and the curious channels carved out
by the melt-waters of the ice and the streams which flowed
along its margins form striking patterns on the slopes of the
higher ground such as the Pentland, Lammermuir and Moorfoot hills.

Scope of the Guide and Further References

All the country thus briefly mentioned has been included in
the day and half-day excursions described in this guide, which
have been chosen to illustrate such of the principal features of
the solid and superficial geology as can conveniently be
reached from Edinburgh. References to maps and other works
providing greater detail are given with each account, but the
visitor will find the quarter-inch to the mile maps of the
Geological Survey (sheets 14, 15, 16 and 17) of value in studying the general geology. One-inch to the mile geological
maps for most of the area are also published by the Geological
Survey, but a few are out of print. Six-inch to the mile maps
of some areas are published; others are available for inspection
in the library of the Geological Survey in Edinburgh, where
the one-inch maps that are out of print may also be consulted.

In the list of maps given at the beginning of the account of
each excursion, the abbreviation 'O.S. One-inch' relates to
sheets of the 'One-inch' Seventh Series Ordnance Survey
Maps of Great Britain; 'G.S. One-inch' refers to the Geological Survey One inch to one mile maps of Scotland. A
further valuable guide is the volume of British Regional
Geology, *The Midland Valley of Scotland*, by M. Macgregor

and A. G. MacGregor, published by the Geological Survey; this contains copious references. Mention must also be made of the admirable exhibits and models displayed in the Royal Scottish Museum.

The areas described in the itineraries are shown on the map below.

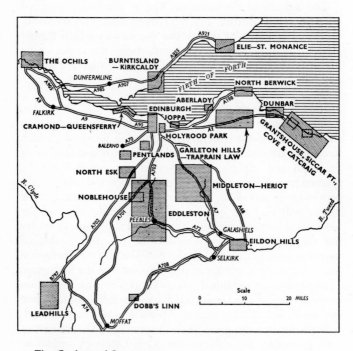

The Geological Succession

The generalized succession of the rocks of the district is given in tabular form on p. 5.

Ordovician rocks form the oldest strata seen on the excursions. They are divided into three groups, of which the

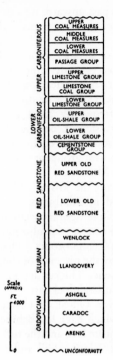

oldest or Arenig Beds consist of graptolite-bearing mudstones with cherts, associated with lavas and tuffs. Some authors claim that Llandeilo cherts and shales occur in places. Succeeding these earlier beds, probably unconformably, are the Caradoc and Ashgill beds, consisting of greywackes, conglomerates and shales, again with graptolites and in some places thin developments of volcanic rocks.

Silurian strata are represented by mudstones, shales, greywackes, conglomerates and grits, the fine-grained members of which also yield graptolites. They are subdivided on fossil evidence into the Llandovery below, with Wenlock beds above. The higher members of the Silurian System developed in other parts of Great Britain appear to have been eroded in Scotland during a long period of earth-movement and denudation which preceded the deposition of the lowest of the Old Red Sandstone beds.

The latter include the Lower Old Red Sandstone which in its lower part consists of sandstones, and coarse-grained conglomerates, succeeded by a great thickness of lavas and tuffs including basalts, andesites, trachytes and rhyolites which forms the craggy ground of the Pentland Hills.

Another period of earth-movement and erosion supervened before the deposition of the Upper Old Red Sandstone which rests with marked unconformity on older rocks. Consisting largely of red sandstones, conglomerates and marls, with some thin calcareous beds known as 'cornstones', the Upper Old

Red Sandstone appears in some areas to pass upwards into the lowest Carboniferous beds but in other districts is perhaps overlapped by these higher strata.

The Carboniferous System consists of a large variety of sediments which are interbedded in places with important volcanic rocks. Perhaps its most interesting feature is the manner in which certain types of sediment such as sandstone, limestone, mudstone, shale and coal frequently recur in a rhythmic manner throughout the succession. Economically they are of the utmost importance as sources of coal, lime, oil-shale and building stone. The three lowest groups are often collectively called Calciferous Sandstone Measures.

The Cementstone Group, which forms the lowest of the Carboniferous strata, is well developed in Edinburgh city, though its strata are only rarely exposed in temporary sections which from time to time reveal them to consist of sandstones, shales and muddy limestones known as 'cementstones'. That volcanoes were active nearby is shown by the presence of thin bands of tuff interbedded with the sediments. Thicker deposits of lava and tuff appear low in the group at Craiglockhart.

The succeeding period of the Lower Oil-Shale Group opened with great volcanic eruptions which have left behind them the thick flows of basalt and mugearite lava and the tuffs interbedded with them now found on Whinny Hill and at Duddingston. The vents through which they were poured now form the Lion's Head and Lion's Haunch on Arthur's Seat—great orifices choked with agglomerate and plugs of lava. Nearby the same rocks form the terraced lavas and tuffs of Calton Hill and the volcanic plug of Edinburgh Castle, while farther afield the similar rocks of Corston Hill are probably of the same age though not necessarily derived from the same volcano.

Both the Lower and the Upper Oil-Shale groups include sandstones, shales, clays and valuable seams of oil-shale, the last named being more common in the upper beds. There are also occasional freshwater limestones and beds of shale with marine fossils.

The Lower Limestone Group, which is the uppermost subdivision of the Lower Carboniferous of Scotland (the equivalent of the Carboniferous Limestone Series of England), contains the thickest beds of limestone found in the Scottish Carboniferous. These are interbedded with shales, often fossiliferous, and sandstones. In the Bathgate Hills this and the succeeding group contain important volcanic beds, though they do not occur in the Midlothian Coalfield.

The Limestone Coal Group, important because of the thick coals contained in its succession of shales, sandstones, seatclays and coal seams, is the Scottish representative of the lowest part of the Millstone Grit Series of England and Wales, a series which also includes the Upper Limestone Group and probably the lower part of the Passage Group.

The Upper Limestone Group is notable for the recurrence of thin limestone beds in a succession of shales, sandstones, seatclays and rare thin coals. Many shelly shales occur.

The Passage Group, formerly known as the Scottish Millstone Grit or Roslin Sandstone, represents but a small portion of the Millstone Grit Series of such areas as the Pennines. The characteristic measures are shales and seatclays, the former often with marine fossils, and thick sandstones. The upper part of the group seems likely to be the equivalent of part of the Lower Coal Measures of the coalfields south of the Border.

The Coal Measures, which are often divided into Lower, Middle and Upper groups, form the younger of the two great coal-bearing formations of the Scottish Carboniferous. They contain a wealth of coal seams, interbedded with seatclays, mudstones, shales, sandstones and a few marine bands and mussel bands, these fossiliferous beds being of great use as indices of horizon, particularly in the search for workable coal seams. The highest Coal Measures are often red-stained.

There is a great break in the sequence of rocks at this stratigraphical level in the Edinburgh district. Apart from a number of volcanic vents, and dykes and sills of basic character, which are post-Carboniferous in age, there are no later rocks exposed. Many of these igneous rocks are worked for roadstone in quarries throughout the district.

As a consequence of the absence from the area of sediments of Permian, Triassic, Jurassic and Tertiary age the long and complicated history of earth-movement and sedimentation represented by those systems can only be inferred from evidence outside the district. There is indeed a very great unconformity between the Coal Measures and the deposits of the Great Ice Age which almost everywhere cover the solid rocks of the neighbourhood of Edinburgh. Of happenings during that enormous interval of time the only glimpses in our area are revealed by volcanic vents, dykes and sills cutting Carboniferous strata, and by comparison with other areas believed to be of Permian age. Of much later date are certain dykes which from their petrographical characters are likely to be Tertiary.

The Glacial Deposits range from tough boulder clay to sand and gravel with delicate bedding. They include examples of terminal and lateral moraines and deltas deposited in temporary lakes from melt-waters of the ice. In places the deposits fill earlier river-valleys as in the case of the Almond and North Esk. They are accompanied by many drainage channels, formed at the margins of the ice sheets, and other modifications of the drainage caused by the presence of thick ice fields, at their maximum probably hundreds, if not thousands of feet thick. These great sheets of ice had a long and complicated history of waxing and waning. After they had melted considerable oscillations in sea-level took place. Thus submergence of the land is recognized by the existence of at least three raised beaches at levels of approximately 100, 50 and 25 ft. above present sea-level, whereas its emergence is indicated by the presence of peat under the deposits of the lowest beach.

Finally, linking up with our own day there are the terraces and alluvium of the modern rivers and the peat mosses which are to be found resting on earlier deposits in numerous places throughout the district.

Acknowledgments

The itineraries included in this guide have been described by numerous authors as listed in the table of contents. The volume has been edited by Messrs G. H. Mitchell, E. K. Walton and Douglas Grant. For permission to reproduce plates and the maps illustrating excursions, which are based wholly or in part on published maps of the Geological Survey, thanks are due to the Director of H.M. Geological Survey and the Controller of H.M. Stationery Office.

CITY OF EDINBURGH

O.S. One-inch Map, Seventh Series, Sheet 62
G.S. One-inch Map, Sheet 32 (Scotland)
Route-maps, p. 12
Six-inch Geological Sheets, Midlothian 1 S.E. and 1A S.W.;
1B S.E. and 1 S.W.; 3 N.E.; 3 S.W.; 3 S.E.

—

FIVE short itineraries illustrating features of geological interest within the city boundaries are described. Together with walking distance and approximate duration they are:

		Time	Walking Distance
(A)	Blackford Hill	3 hours	2½ miles
(B)	Craiglockhart and Colinton	3 hours	3 miles
(C)	The Dean	1½ hours	1 mile
(D)	Wardie and Granton Shore	2 hours (plus collecting time)	2 miles
(E)	The Castle Hill	1½ hours	1 mile

A short note is also appended on the Royal Scottish Museum.

Excursion A—Blackford Hill
(Route-map p. 12)

Proceed by bus route 39 or 41 to the Blackford Pond entrance of Blackford Hill Park in Cluny Gardens.

The Lower Old Red Sandstone Volcanics of Blackford Hill

form the northern limit of the volcanics of the Pentland Anticline, and are wrapped around to the north by sandstones of Upper Old Red Sandstone age. At the park entrance the junction of the volcanics with the sandstone crosses Cluny Gardens obliquely and continues south-westward under the Blackford Pond.

1. Quarry at Blackford Pond: Base of Blackford Volcanic Sequence

Enter the park and follow the footpath which skirts the south side of the pond. A few yards beyond the pond there is a small disused quarry on the left hand side. Here a thin bed of agglomerate is exposed which is overlain by a massive fine-grained, basic andesite lava and is underlain by trachytic lava of the Braid Hills suite. This quarry is situated at the north-western extremity of the hill and since the general dip is north-easterly it exposes the base of the Blackford Hill volcanic sequence. The hill itself appears to be carved from a single flow of basic andesite whose base rests on the agglomerate here exposed.

2. Blackford Pond to Rustic Bridge: Crag and Tail Featuring, Post-Glacial Cut

Continue along the footpath which follows the western limits of the park. The boundary wall to the right of the footpath (2a) contains, especially in its northern part, good samples of Upper Old Red Sandstone rocks. These blocks, which were probably taken from an old quarry to the north of Blackford Hill, exhibit well the red sandstone and corn-stones of the local succession.

Follow the footpath towards the summit of the rise about 500 yd. south of the Old Quarry (2b) noting the topographic forms due to Crag and Tail featuring. Ice moved from the west towards the east and impinged upon the western face of the 'crag' formed by the Blackford Hill andesite. Ice diverted northwards excavated the hollow occupied by the Blackford

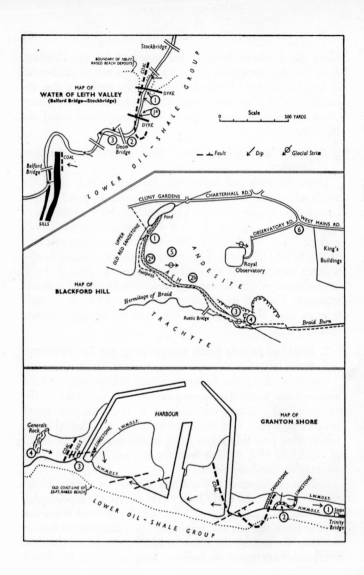

Pond and the suburban railway. The path itself, together with the field and allotments which adjoin the park, occupy the hollow gouged by the arrested ice to the west of the crag. Before reaching the summit of the rise, however, note the deep, steep-sided trough of the tree-filled Hermitage of Braid which cuts across the ice-excavated hollow and approaches the footpath from the right. This chasm was probably cut by a glacial overflow channel which formed after movement of the ice had ceased and when the ice field was retreating northward from the northern face of the Pentlands. The margin of the ice must then have blocked the northern drainage of the Braid Burn and diverted its waters eastward, cutting the gorge of Hermitage of Braid. Follow the footpath over the rise and descend into the valley of the Braid Burn. It will be seen, as the Rustic Bridge is approached, that the burn leaves the confines of the Hermitage and continues eastward in a broader valley. This was excavated at the time of Crag and Tail formation by the ice which was diverted towards the south. The Braid Burn, however, has excavated a deeper channel in the northern part of the broad valley, the southern wall of the valley being still covered by Boulder Clay. The change in profile is well seen on the southern slopes of the valley, between the upper and gentler slope due to ice excavation, and the lower steeper slope due to down cutting by the Braid Burn in continuance of its deep Hermitage of Braid channel.

3. Blackford Hill Old Quarry: Old Red Sandstone Andesite

From the Rustic Bridge follow the footpath eastwards by the burnside until a gateway is passed when, on the left will be seen an old disused quarry where good specimens of the Blackford Hill Andesite may be collected, also specimens of jasper and chlorite, minerals which fill veins intersecting the andesite. The rock is a dark-grey, finely crystalline and non-vesicular andesite weathering to a reddish colour. The few porphyritic crystals which it contains are plagioclase felspar, biotite and augite. In thin section it shows well-marked fluxion structure. The quarry was previously extensively used for road metal but access to the quarry which lies beyond the Old Quarry is forbidden.

4. The Agassiz Rock: 'This is the work of ice'

Immediately to the east of the Old Quarry lies the *Agassiz Rock*. The site is marked by a Nature Conservancy notice since it occupies an important place in the history of glacial geology in Scotland. Here the andesite cliff has been undercut to form a cave which is grooved and striated like the over-hanging cliff. In 1840 Charles Maclaren brought the celebrated Swiss geologist Louis Agassiz to see these features which Agassiz recognized as being the work of land ice, the first such recognition in Scotland. While Agassiz' opinion provided a stimulus to Scottish glacial geologists to recognize similar evidence elsewhere as the work of land ice, the evidence at the Agassiz Rock is capable of other interpretation such as slickensiding and undercutting by glacial melt waters carried by the Braid Burn.

5. Blackford Hill Summit: Viewpoint, Crag and Tail

Retrace the route to the Rustic Bridge and ascend the hill by following the footpath to the right. From the summit a fine view of the district is obtained. Land forms due to Crag and Tail featuring, which have already been noticed, may be seen again from this vantage point while the 'Tail', composed of boulder clay covering Lower Old Red volcanics and Upper Old Red sediments, may now be seen extending to the east.

6. Harrison Arch: Location of Porphyry of Carnethy Type

Descend eastwards by way of the Royal Observatory and Observatory Road to the Harrison Arch through which pass and turning right follow West Mains Road. In the walls of the district to the east of Blackford Hill, blocks of porphyritic basalt or porphyry of Carnethy type may be observed. These are locally derived from a lava flow which overlies the andesite lava of Blackford Hill. The rock has been seen *in situ* in temporary exposures and is only a few feet below the surface in the neighbourhood of the Harrison Arch.

The Grant Institute of Geology of the University of Edinburgh is seen on the right of West Mains Road. Turn left at the junction with Mayfield Road along which the 42 bus route passes into the city centre.

Excursion B—Craiglockhart and Colinton

Proceed to Craiglockhart Station, bus routes 9, 10 and 27.

1. Craiglockhart Railway Cutting: Colinton Fault

The Colinton Fault, which here trends in a north-easterly direction, cuts across the railway cutting to the south of Craiglockhart Station platform where dark shales of the Calciferous Sandstone (of Wardie and Granton type) are downfaulted against sandstones of Upper Old Red Sandstone age. The rocks of the district occupy the western limb of the Pentland Anticline, their general dip being towards the north-west. At the fault the Carboniferous shales are steeply inclined. The fault may be viewed in the north-east bank of the cutting from Craiglockhart Terrace at the point where the Terrace turns away from the railway, but may be better seen from the University playing fields at times when the field is open. The gate of the field is at the angle of Craiglockhart Terrace. The south-west bank of the cutting may be seen from a footpath leading from Craiglockhart Station to Craighouse Road. Access to the path may be obtained when the station is open. In the Upper Old Red Sandstone rocks between the Colinton fault and Craighouse Road, subsidiary faults may be seen and sandstone dykes penetrate into the Upper Old Red shales.

2. Craiglockhart Ponds: Colinton Fault Scarp

The Fault Scarp of the Colinton Fault is well seen from Lockharton Crescent where it overlooks Craiglockhart Ponds. To reach the Crescent follow Colinton Road south-westward and turn left into Lockharton Gardens which leads to Lockharton Crescent. The basalt lava of Craiglockhart Hill is here faulted against softer shales and sandstones of Calciferous Sandstone age and as a result of differential weathering the scarp forms a prominent topographic feature.

3. Glenlockhart: Craiglockhart Volcanics

Return to Colinton Road by way of Lockharton Crescent and follow it uphill for half a mile and turning left into Glenlockhart Road proceed for an eighth of a mile to the western limit of the Craiglockhart Golf Course. From the road at this point a good section of the volcanics may be seen in Wester Craiglockhart Hill to the right of Glenlockhart Road. Here about 100 ft. of bedded volcanic ash is succeeded by a massive columnar lava of similar thickness, the whole series dipping towards the north-west. The junction of the lava with the ash is slightly transgressive possibly owing to disturbance of the underlying ash by the overflowing lava. The tuffs are basaltic with isolated crystals of augite and olivine. The lava is the type 'Craiglockhart Basalt' widely found at or near the base of the Carboniferous system in Scotland. It is a basalt with large phenocrysts of olivine and augite but not of plagioclase felspar. The slaggy top of the lava flow is approached before the volcanic series is cut off by the Colinton Fault.

4. Redhall Mill: Wardie Beds

Sediments of the lower part of the Calciferous Sandstone are well seen in the Colinton Dell section of the Water of Leith. From Glenlockhart Road cross Colinton Road into Craiglockhart Avenue, taking the second turning on the left

Arthur's Seat showing Lion's Head and Lion's Haunch Vents and south-eastern termination of Salisbury Crags Sill

into Craiglockhart Drive South. Follow Craiglockhart Drive South for three quarters of a mile, pass Redhall Children's Home on the right and proceed to Redhall Mill. From Redhall Mill to Colinton the path leads through Colinton Dell where the Water of Leith cuts through the following sequence.

4. Poor Oil Shales and dark shales.
3. Green Sandy Beds with Pebble Beds and Green Shales.
2. Thin Limestones with *Camarotoechia* etc.
1. Light Reddish Sandstones.

On the lower side of the weir on the Water of Leith just above Redhall Mill rocks of group 3 are exposed. Here a sandstone with bands of conglomerate containing pebbles of radiolarian chert crops out and under it a green shale containing detached pinnules of *Cardiopteris*. Shales of the overlying group 4 are seen below the footbridge which crosses the Water of Leith below the Weir.

5. Colinton Church: Pre-Glacial Water of Leith, Post-Glacial Cut

Follow the footpath southwards up the valley to the bend of the river at Colinton Manse where reddish sandstones of group 1 are exposed in the cliff on the opposite side of the river. They are seen to form a sharp anticline.

The steep-sided gorge of Colinton Dell represents a post-glacial cut by the Water of Leith. It is probable that the pre-glacial course of the river left the present valley opposite Colinton Church where the river now changes direction. Continue to Colinton Village by Dell Road. Bus routes 9, 10 run from Colinton to the City Centre.

Excursion C—The Dean
(*Route-map p.12*)

The Excursion starts at Stockbridge on bus routes 24 and 29 from the City Centre.

1. Stockbridge, St. Bernard's Well: Granton Sandstone and Shale Beds, Quartz-dolerite Dykes

Between Drumsheugh and Stockbridge the Water of Leith has cut its course through the sandstones and shales of the Granton Beds, which belong to the Lower Oil-Shale Group. The valley exposes what is virtually a strike section of the beds which here dip westwards and occupy the west limb of the 'St Andrews' Square Anticline' which is an expression within the city of the Pentland Anticline. This anticline is followed to the west by the Granton-Wardie Syncline.

Proceed to St Bernard's Well by way of Saunders Street, which follows the Water of Leith upstream from the bridge at Stockbridge, and the footpath by the waterside when the Dean Park is reached. St Bernard's Well was a sulphurous medicinal well whose waters were prized for many years, as the 18th century classic well-house shows. In the river bank opposite the well, a quartz-dolerite dyke is exposed cutting shales and flaggy sandstones of the Granton Beds. The dyke is 3 to 4 ft. in thickness and trends west-north-westwards.

Skirt the well by the waterside, and follow the path upstream for 25 yd. where a current-bedded sandstone of the Granton Beds with good ripple-marks is well seen dipping westwards.

Return to St Bernard's Well, mount the steps to the main pathway and, turning right, follow the path upstream for 200 yd. when, in the river under a small building to the right of the path (1a), another quartz-dolerite dyke cutting a bed of sandstone is exposed. This dyke is some 10 ft. in thickness and its trend is parallel to the St Bernard's Well dyke.

A poor coal occurs in the river bed some 350 ft. above the second dyke and some 100 yd. downstream from the Dean Bridge. Unfortunately access to this coal is not possible.

2. The Dean Bridge: Granton Beds Shales

Follow the path upstream for a further 100 yd. when on the left-hand side, in the cliff below the Dean Bridge, there occurs a fine exposure of shales with ironstone nodules and sandstone above. It is possible to collect from the shales at this exposure where, in addition to plant and entomostracan remains, *Naiadites obesus* (R. Eth. jnr.) has been obtained.

3. Miller Row: Granton Beds/Wardie Shales Junction, Post-Glacial Cut

Passing under the Dean Bridge reach the view point by the ornamental mill-wheels in Miller Row. Here the Water of Leith occupies a westerly loop of its course and the shales and sandstones of the Granton Beds, which were seen at the last exposure to be dipping westward at some 15°, plunge into the river bed and are succeeded on the opposite cliff, under the church, by 180 ft. of bituminous blaes. From fossil evidence obtained further along the strike at Drumsheugh, it is known that these bituminous blaes belong to the succeeding Wardie Shales.

From this view point the post-glacial cut of the Dean gorge is well seen. Upstream from Belford Bridge, which lies $\frac{1}{4}$-mile above the Dean Bridge, the Water of Leith occupies a valley filled with deep boulder clay which presumably represents its pre-glacial course. At Stockbridge the river meanders over the 100-ft. Raised Beach deposits. At the Dean, however, the valley is steep-sided and cut in rock with no boulder clay filling. It is probable that in post-glacial times the river was deflected from its original course by the resistant dolerite sills at Belford Bridge causing the river, heavy with glacial melt water and rejuvenated by the rising land level, to cut the spectacular gorge of Dean.

Follow Miller Row to the small bridge and, turning left, ascend Bell's Brae to Queensferry Road which leads to the West End of Princes Street.

Excursion D—Wardie and Granton Shore
(*Route-map p.* 12)

The excursion may be undertaken only at low water. Proceed to Trinity Bridge, bus routes 22, 16. Access to the

shore is by the stairway at Trinity Bridge. Turn left on reaching the shore and pass the building situated some yards west
of the stairway on the landward side.

1. Shore westwards from Trinity Bridge: Wardie Shales

The Wardie Shales belong to the Calciferous Sandstone
Measures of the Carboniferous and succeed the Granton sandstones which will be seen at the western end of the shore
section. For some 400 yd. westward from Trinity Bridge,
black blaes are exposed on the shore having a gentle dip
towards the east. Their total exposed thickness is some 70 ft.
The blaes contain ironstone nodules which, at an early date
were used as an ore by the Carron Company. These nodules
have yielded a rich fossil fish fauna including the following
species: *Acanthodes sulcatus* Ag., *Rhizodus hibberti* (Ag.),
Gonatodus punctatus (Ag.), *Elonichthys robisoni* (Hibbert),
Elonichthys striatus (Ag.), *Rhadinichthys ornatissimus* (Ag.),
Rhadinichthys carinatus (Ag.), *Rhadinichthys brevis* Traquair,
Rhadinichthys ferox Traquair, *Nematoptychius greenocki* (Ag.),
Eurynotus crenatus Ag., *Wardichthys cyclosoma* Traquair. Most
of the fossils have been obtained at the Trinity Bridge end of
the section.

2. Shore East of the East Breakwater of Granton Harbour: Wardie Coal, Limestone

Continuing westwards it will be found that between 400 yd.
and 500 yd. from the Trinity Bridge steps, the beds form a
small syncline closely followed to the west by the eastern
limb of an anticline. The succession at this point is given as
follows:

Black blaes with ironstone nodules (exposed from Trinity Bridge)	70 ft.
Limestone, dark brown with entomostraca	4 in.
Tuff, pale	2 in.
Blaes	6 in.

Limestone, with entomostraca, coaly plant remains, and lamellibranchs	6 in.
Coal seam (Wardie Coal)	3 ft.

The coal seam has been dug out along the strike and is thus difficult to find, but the associated limestone succession may be traced. The most westerly outcrop of the limestone occurs 300 yd. east of the eastern breakwater of Granton Harbour. It is underlain to the west by a thin shale and a thin sandstone, after which the succession is disturbed by faulting and obscured by beach deposits.

Having reached the beach, leave the foreshore by way of the tunnel under the railway which gives access to Lower Granton Road. Turn right and pass Granton Harbour by way of Lower Granton Road, Granton Square and Shore Road and beyond the western breakwater return to the foreshore. In the harbour the anticline seen to adjoin the eastern breakwater is succeeded to the west by a syncline which repeats to the west of the harbour the succession which has been noticed to the east. The beds in the harbour cannot now be seen.

3. Shore West of the West Breakwater of Granton Harbour: Wardie Coal, Limestone

The Wardie Coal with its associated limestone occurs some 100 yd. west of the western breakwater. The beds are again dipping eastwards and between the breakwater and the limestone, black blaes containing ironstone nodules with fish remains are again seen, but are here intruded by numerous thin olivine-dolerite sills. The details of the succession to the west of the harbour are given as follows:

Black Blaes with ironstone nodules penetrated by sills.	
Limestone, dark with pyrites, carbonised plant remains, *Lingula* and entomostraca.	$2\frac{1}{2}$ in.

Shale, with dark brown streak made up of crushed
    entomostraca.   4 in.
Limestone, dark, conchoidal fracture, with lamelli-
    branchs, *Lingula* and plant fragments.   4 in.
Coal seam (Wardie Coal).   3 ft.

4. The General's Rock: Wardie Shales, Granton Sandstone Beds

To the west of the coal the basal portion of the Wardie
Shales is exposed and consists of 180 ft. of dark blaes, partly
bituminous, with thin ferruginous ribs. The top of the
underlying Granton Sandstone Beds crops out in the General's
Rock 300 yd. west of the western breakwater. Return by
Shore Road to Granton Square from which bus routes 8, 9,
10, 14, 16, 17, 19 and 22 leave for the city centre.

Excursion E—The Castle Hill

The Excursion starts at the Half Moon Battery in the Castle.
During the summer months a number 32 bus may be taken
from the foot of the Mound to the Castle Esplanade, otherwise
walk via the Mound and Lawnmarket.

1. Within Castle Walls: Crag and Tail, Plug/Carboniferous Junction

The Castle Hill and the Royal Mile form a classic example
of Crag and Tail featuring. The ice sheet moved from the
west and impinged on the western face of the basaltic plug on
which the Castle is built. Ice was deflected towards the north
and excavated the valley now occupied by Princes Street
Gardens and the railway line leading to Waverley Station. Ice
which was deflected to the south excavated the valley now
occupied by the Grassmarket and the Cowgate. The 'tail',
composed of sediments protected by the 'crag' and overlying
drift, forms the gentle slope of the Royal Mile leading from
the Castle to the Palace of Holyrood House. These features are

well seen from the vantage points of the Half Moon Battery and the Fore Wall Battery.

The Fore Well, situated at the northern end of the Half Moon Battery, marks the position of the junction of the basaltic plug with the lower Carboniferous sediments which lie to the east. The basalt may be seen at the summit of the Castle Hill between the National War Memorial and the Half Moon Battery, which is itself built on sediments as will appear later. Descend by the steps adjoining Argyll's Tower and turning right pass through the Portcullis gate. Some ten yards short of the Inner Barrier the northern part of the eastern junction may be seen in the right hand gutter of the roadway. Here the basalt and greenish-grey Carboniferous marl are exposed close together, the marl having been hardened by contact with the basalt. Continue down the roadway and on reaching the souvenir shop opposite the guardhouse look at the cliff behind it towards the Half Moon Battery when it is possible to see the sediments upon which the Battery is built. They lie between the junction with the basaltic plug, and the Castle Fault to the east, and consist of greenish marly shales dipping very steeply inwards towards the basalt. This dip was beneficial in accumulating water for the Fore Well.

2. Johnston Terrace: Plug/Carboniferous Sediments Junction, Castle Fault

Leaving the Castle cross the Esplanade and descend the stairs to the right at Castle Wynd North. On reaching Johnston Terrace turn right and proceed downhill for 200 yd. Above the grassy slope to the right, in the corner formed by the Half Moon Battery and the Old Palace, the southern part of the eastern junction is well seen. It is vertical and the Castle Fault lies only a few feet to the east. The dip of the sediments near the junction is steep but the sandstones under the esplanade, which are to the east of the Castle Fault, are dipping gently away from the plug. Continuing down Johnston Terrace the margin of the basalt rises as a steep cliff. The basalt which composes it is microporphyritic and of Dalmeny type. In thin section it shows small altered olivines and augites embedded in a mesh of felspar crystals with microlithic augite and magnetite granules.

3. West Princes Street Gardens: Plug/Carboniferous Sediments Junction, Glacial Striae

Follow the base of the Castle Rock by entering West Princes Street Gardens by the gate on the right twenty yards short of the bridge carrying Johnston Terrace over Kingstables Road. On the left of the footpath is the valley excavated by ice whose easterly movement had been arrested by the west face of the Castle Rock. On the right the western junction of the plug with the Carboniferous sediments may be followed. Where it is first seen the contact is with sandstone, then some 300 ft. to the north-west with sandstone and marl and then another 200 ft. to the north with marly shales. Follow the footpath to the northern face of the Castle Rock where marginal chilling of the basalt is well displayed.

Glacial moulding may be seen at a height of some 15 ft. on the northern face of the plug where it most closely approaches the railway. Near the ruins of the Old Well House glacial striae occur with an approximately east-west orientation. Looking westward from the Well House there is evidence in the plug of horizontal columnar jointing controlled by cooling against a vertical margin.

The railway traverses the site of a post-glacial lake which occupied the ice-excavated valley between the Castle and Princes Street. Between A.D. 1450 and 1816 the site was occupied by a smaller artificial lake called the Nor' Loch.

Access to Princes Street may be gained by way of one of the footbridges which span the railway.

The Royal Scottish Museum

The Museum is situated in Chambers Street, which may be reached from Princes Street by way of the Mound and George IV Bridge or the East End and the Bridges. Opening hours are weekdays 10 a.m. to 5 p.m., Sundays 2 p.m. to 5 p.m. Admission free.

Six galleries are of special interest to geologists visiting the museum. On the ground floor is the Extinct Animal Hall dealing in a popular manner with the life of past ages and showing how it is related to our living fauna, and the Hall of Mining and Metallurgy which exhibits by specimens and models the history of coal mining in Scotland up to modern times and displays the ores and uses of the economic metals. The latter display is mounted by the museum's Technological Department.

Four geological galleries are found on the second floor at the east end of the building. The first houses the Scottish Mineral Collection which includes the cabinets of such famous Scottish mineralogists as M. F. Heddle and P. Dudgeon. Exhibited here also are geological block models of localities representative of the major types of Scottish geology. Those of purely local interest are the Arthur's Seat Model on a scale of 24 in. to 1 mile and the model of the Midlothian Coal Basin and the Pentland Anticline on a scale of 6 in. to 1 mile. The second gallery is devoted to Scottish Regional Geology and displays, by means of specimens, maps and diagrams, the geology of the five regions into which the Geological Survey have divided Scotland—The Northern Highlands, The Grampian Highlands, The Tertiary Volcanic Districts, The Midland Valley and the Southern Uplands. Also shown in this gallery is an Introductory Collection dealing with minerals, rocks and rock structures. The third gallery is devoted to a General Mineral Collection in which is displayed a collection of minerals and gems of rare quality from throughout the world. The fourth gallery houses a display of vertebrate and invertebrate fossils arranged systematically.

The collections in the care of the museum's Department of Geology date from 1812, when Professor Robert Jameson occupied the Chair of Natural History in the University of Edinburgh, and have since been liberally added to. Of special importance are the Traquair, Powrie, Duff and Hugh Miller collections of fossil fishes; the Armstrong, Neilson, Dunlop and Coutts collections of Carboniferous invertebrates; the James Wright collection of Crinoids; the C. W. Peach collection of fossils; the Hardie and Henderson collections of Pentland Hills fossils; and the Heddle, Dudgeon, Brown, Wilson, and Craig Christie collections of minerals.

REFERENCES

Blackford Hill

CAMPBELL, R., 1932. Note on the Occurrence of 'Carnethy Porphyry' at Blackford Hill. *Trans. Edin. Geol. Soc.*, vol. 12, p. 387.

COCKBURN, A. M., 1956. Notes on the Geology of the Eastern Slopes of Blackford Hill, Edinburgh. *Trans. Edin. Geol. Soc.*, vol. 16, pp. 307–312.

Craiglockhart and Colinton

TAIT, D., 1916. On Bores for Water and Medicinal Wells in the Wardie Shales, near Edinburgh. *Trans. Edin. Geol. Soc.*, vol. 10, pp. 316–325.

The Dean

HENDERSON, J., 1884. On Rock Sections exposed in cutting for the Suburban Railway: with observations on the Geology of the District around Edinburgh. *Trans. Edin. Geol. Soc.*, vol. 5, pp. 71–82.

TAIT, D., 1916. On Bores for Water and Medicinal Wells in the Wardie Shales, near Edinburgh. *Trans. Edin. Geol. Soc.*, vol. 10, pp. 316–325.

Wardie and Granton Shore

TAIT, D., 1925. The Rocks between Leith and Granton with Historical Notes on the working of the Wardie Coal. *Trans. Edin. Geol. Soc.*, vol. 11, pp. 346–351.

The Castle Hill

TAIT, D., 1945. Geological Notes on (*a*) The Nor' Loch and (*b*) The Fore Well in Edinburgh Castle. *Trans. Edin. Geol. Soc.*, vol. 14, pp. 28–33.

C. D. WATERSTON

ARTHUR'S SEAT

O.S. One-inch Map, Seventh Series, Sheet 62
G.S. One-inch Map, Sheet 32
Route-map, p. 32

—

LESS than a mile from the city centre, the remnants of the long-extinct volcano of Arthur's Seat rise from the low ground on which Edinburgh is built. Part of the volcano has been lost through erosion and part has been buried under younger rocks; enough, however, is exposed to allow us to study the vulcanicity in some detail, especially as the removal of much of the superstructure has laid bare the internal parts of the volcano. The largest volcanic remnant lies within the Holyrood Park where it culminates in Arthur's Seat (823 ft.), the hill from which the volcano takes its name. To the north and west smaller remnants build the Calton Hill and the Castle Rock. The volcano was active early in the Carboniferous Period. The volcanic rocks rest on strata high in the Cementstone Group and are covered by the lowermost sedimentary member of the Oil-Shale Group—the Abbeyhill Shales.

The first eruption of the Arthur's Seat Volcano was made into shallow water in which rocks of the Cementstone Group had accumulated, but, early in the activity, the higher parts of the cone were raised above water-level and colonized by land plants. Their fossilized remains are found to-day in the ashes and agglomerates. The deposition of chemically precipitated limestone high on the cone in the middle stages of the activity, and the final burial of the entire volcano by waterlaid sediment, indicate that the greater part of the cone was submerged during most of the volcano's life; this contention is supported by the presence locally of well-bedded ashes between most of the lava flows. Thus, although the lavas were erupted subærially, much of their descent of the cone was made below water. No trace of pillow structure, however, has ever been observed, but some of the higher lavas have been partially albitized and carbonated and are now transitional between normal basalts and spilites.

As exposed to-day, the Arthur's Seat Volcano consists of five vents (the composite Lion's Head and Lion's Haunch vents, the basalt-filled Castle Rock and Pulpit Rock vents and the agglomerate-filled Crags Vent), three portions of the cone (the Whinny and Calton Hills and an area near Duddingston) and a number of sills and dykes. The Salisbury Crags Sill and two small dykes were intruded long after the volcano became extinct.

Whinny Hill provides the most complete and accessible sequence of lavas. Lava 1, believed from petrographic evidence to have been erupted from the Castle Rock Vent, forms the Long Row and its northern downfaulted portion, the Haggis Knowe. Above the lava there lies a considerable thickness of mixed ash and sediment known collectively as the Lower Ash of the Dry Dam; this contains at least two bands of precipitated limestone, the lower containing irregular masses of chert. The ash, most probably derived from the Lion's Head Vent, is covered by Lava 2 which was erupted from the same orifice within which its feeding conduit is preserved. There followed the formation of a further bed of intermingled ash and sediment in which volcanic bombs are prominent—the Upper Ash of the Dry Dam. After the accumulation of the ash, a parasitic vent—the Pulpit Rock Vent—some distance down the northern slopes of the cone, emitted Lava 3. Later Lava 4 was erupted from the Lion's Head Vent at the apex of the cone and descended normally until diverted around the obstacle formed by Lava 3. Lava 4 is only seen on the southern part of Whinny Hill to-day, its northern continuation having been diverted out of the present plane of exposures by Lava 3. Lava 4 was the last flow to be erupted from the Lion's Head Vent for the residue of the flow remaining in the vent blocked the orifice on consolidation. All further activity of the Arthur's Seat Volcano was focused on the Lion's Haunch Vent from which the remaining nine lavas (5 to 13) of Whinny Hill were erupted. These flows lie in normal succession, one above another, the contacts of the flows being rarely marked by any considerable ash bed.

The remnant of the cone of the Arthur's Seat Volcano exposed on the northern shores of Duddingston Loch differs extensively from the remnant which forms Whinny Hill and, apart from Lava 1, the successions cannot be correlated with any certainty.

The Calton Hill succession shows a general resemblance to that of the Whinny Hill and though not included in the present itineraries it may be easily followed by ascending the steps at the east end of Waterloo Place and proceeding eastwards over the hill. At the base alternations of ash and sediment occur; these represent the two ash beds of the Dry Dam for the equivalents of Lavas 1 and 2 of the Whinny Hill are not found on the Calton Hill. Above the ashes lie two lavas of Craiglockhart basalt, the lower closely resembling Lava 3 of the Whinny Hill. Lavas 4, 5, 6 and 7 of the Whinny Hill are not found, their temporal equivalent being a thick bed of ash containing an unsorted assemblage of boulders, blocks and bombs of basalt. Above this there lies a group of three lavas of Markle basalt separated by thin ash-beds—the local equivalents of Lavas 8, 9 and 10 of the Whinny Hill. On the highest Markle flow lies another ash-bed which, in turn, is overlain by a group of three mugearite lavas, again separated by ash-beds; these flows are the approximate equivalents in time of Whinny Hill Lavas 11 and 12. The highest mugearite lava of the Calton Hill is directly covered by the Abbeyhill Shales.

Of the five vents of the volcano, that of the Lion's Haunch

is by far the largest and most complex. It is infilled chiefly by
a red agglomerate consisting of a fine-grained red matrix of
decomposed basaltic ash in which lie basaltic and sedimentary
blocks up to ten feet in length. Within the agglomerate there
occur at least seven small lava flows, of basalt or mugearite,
which were erupted and confined within the crater walls. A
common associate of these flows is a bedded red tuffaceous
sandstone, pointing to the existence of temporary crater lakes
during periods of quiescence in the vulcanicity. A mass of
Dunsapie basalt forms the summit of the Lion's Haunch and
partly rests on and partly cuts across the underlying agglomerate. This mass is the remnant of a one-time lava lake which
probably once filled and blocked the Lion's Haunch Vent and
brought the surface activity of the volcano to a close.

Several basaltic intrusions lie in the Lion's Haunch Vent.
In the east there occurs the marginal intrusion of Dunsapie
Hill, the type locality for Dunsapie basalt. The mass was intruded into screes which once lay banked against the inner
crater wall. In the west of the vent there crops out at Samson's
Ribs an intrusion, again of Dunsapie basalt, which ascended
along the wall of the vent and extended in a number of irregular tongues into the crater infilling.

The other three vents seen in the Holyrood Park are simpler
in constitution. The Lion's Head Vent, now partly truncated
by the later and larger Lion's Haunch Vent, appears to have
been originally cylindrical in form and largely infilled by a
fine agglomerate, through which penetrated the feeding conduits for Lavas 2 and 4; these conduits are now filled by
Craiglockhart and Dalmeny basalt respectively. The Pulpit
Rock Vent—the orifice of Lava 3—is a small plug of Craiglockhart basalt. The Crags Vent is filled with fine-grained agglomerate containing fragments of basalt similar to Lavas 1 and
2 of Whinny Hill. No higher flows have contributed fragments and it is probable that this vent ceased its activity shortly
after the eruption of Lava 2.

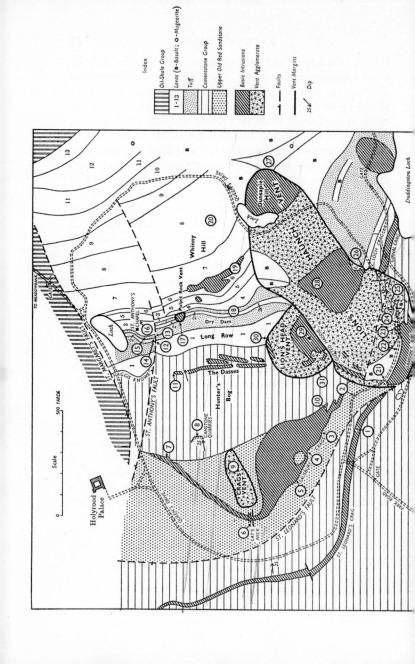

The intrusions associated with the vulcanicity, other than those in the vents, include a sill, which has been divided into three portions now forming the St Leonard's Crag, the Dasses and the Girnal Crag. The probable feeder of the sill is situated at the Dasses where some dyke-like contacts may be seen. A second sill, known as the Whinny Hill Intrusion, occurs between Lavas 6 and 7.

Two intrusions of later date than the Arthur's Seat vulcanicity occur in the Holyrood Park. The larger is the well-known teschenite sill of the Salisbury Crags of mid-Carboniferous age. To the north of the Cat's Nick the sill is cut by a later (Permo-Carboniferous) quartz-dolerite dyke which contains a large strip xenolith of the sill rock.

After the final extinction of the volcano it was covered by thousands of feet of sediments. Earth-movements folded the strata and imparted to the buried Arthur's Seat Volcano a general eastward dip of between 20° and 30°. Many faults cut the sediments and the volcanic rocks. The sedimentary cover of the volcano was removed by prolonged denudation which culminated in the distinctive erosion caused by the Pleistocene ice-sheet. The ice moved from west to east across the area; the hard rocks of the Arthur's Seat Volcano were left as high land while the soft surrounding sediments were more extensively planed away. The easterly dip of the volcanic rocks caused the ice-sheet to produce the present-day topography of westward facing cliffs backed by gentle easterly slopes. The famous crag-and-tail structure of the Castle Rock and the High Street is the best known of these phenomena, but similar land forms have been produced at the Salisbury Crags and the Calton Hill. A fine *roche moutonée* has been preserved in the Queen's Drive and glacial striæ can be observed at several localities.

Excursion A—The Salisbury Crags. 2½ hours

Access to the Holyrood Park is gained by the Park Road Gate. The following localities are then visited in succession:

D

Salisbury Crags. Chilled lower contact of sill with baked Upper Old Red Sandstone Sediments

1. St Leonard's Crag

In a low interrupted line of cliffs to the south of the Queen's Drive the St Leonard's Sill is exposed. The central member of Dunsapie basalt, seen elsewhere, is absent and the sill, about 15 ft. in thickness, consists throughout of a brownish-red, markedly altered mugearite containing sparse plagioclase phenocrysts and small vesicles.

2. Queen's Drive: Old Red Sandstone Sediments

On the north side of the Queen's Drive white or pale red sandstones and marls are exposed. From the roadside exposure several tons of rock were blasted and removed for examination; on careful search several scales of *Holoptychius nobilissimus* were found, thus proving the beds to belong to the Upper Old Red Sandstone (*See* Peach, 1921, p. 6)

3. Salisbury Crags: Hutton's Section

The justly famous Hutton's Section of the base of Salisbury Crags Sill is found towards the south-eastern end of the escarpment, and provided Hutton and his followers with telling evidence in favour of magmatic intrusion in the great argument with the Wernerians in the eighteenth century. Beneath the sill lie well-bedded Upper Old Red Sandstone strata, alternately red and white. The sill transgresses the bedding conspicuously in two places. At the first the sediment against the transgression is crumpled; at the other a wedge of teschenite has been intruded beneath a block of sediment, rotating it upwards from its original position and partly engulfing it in the sill. At the western end of the section, the teschenite immediately above the contact has been chilled to a glassy skin up to $\frac{1}{2}$ in. thick, which has now been devitrified to a greenish material. Above the glass the teschenite is very fine in grain but coarsens markedly upwards. In the rock-face to the south-east of Hutton's section rafts of sediment, many feet in length and a foot or so in thickness, can be seen high in the sill. The rafts are not distorted and lie parallel to the strata below the sill. Still further to the south-west, syenitic segregation veins up to two inches in thickness cut the sill.

Note: Hutton's section is protected by the Ministry of Works and the use of hammers here is forbidden.

4. Hutton's Rock

At the north-western end of the largest disused quarry in the Salisbury Crags Sill, a small isolated rock stands close to the path. Owing its preservation to the interest of Hutton, it is now known as Hutton's Rock. Here teschenite which has been extensively hæmatitized is cut by a vein of impure hæmatite several inches in thickness.

5. Sill-Sandstone Relations

Here, at the foot of the Salisbury Crags, a mass of red sand-stone is bordered above and on the east by the sill. Its other contacts are not seen and it is therefore uncertain whether it is a true xenolith or a tongue of the underlying sediments projecting into the sill. The intrusion of the sill has crumpled the sandstone and has locally produced slight faulting.

6. Cat's Nick: Fault, Quartz-dolerite Dyke

At the Cat's Nick a small east-west fault with a downthrow of a few feet to the north cuts the Salisbury Crags Sill and the underlying sediments. The teschenite close to the fault is much decomposed and shows spheroidal weathering. A few yards farther to the north, a quartz-dolerite dyke traverses the sill. The dyke, a few feet in width, is much finer in grain than the sill and shows a distinct joint pattern. Just above the path it contains a large strip-xenolith of teschenite.

7. Sill: Upper Contact

In a prominent embayment into the line of the Crags, the upper contact of the teschenite sill is exposed. The teschenite decreases markedly in granularity and becomes vesicular as the contact is approached; the sediments above, white sandstones of the Cementstone Group, show little alteration other than a slight induration.

8. Camstone Quarries: Cementstone Group Sediments

In the disused Camstone Quarries sandstones, shales and cementstones of the Cementstone Group dip eastwards at 25°. Well developed sun-cracks, ripple-marks and worm-tracks occur and from the cementstones the small crustacean *Estheria peachi* has been obtained.

9. Crags Vent: Agglomerate

A low mound marks the position of the Crags Vent and is bounded by a very broken scarp in which the fine-grained agglomerate of the vent is exposed.

10. Sill: Upper Contact, Tachylyte Veins

At the top of the main cliff of the Salisbury Crags, the teschenite sill very close to its upper contact is exposed and is seen to contain vesicles which, in places, are arranged in trains as a result of late magmatic movement. Patches of altered sediment, of supposed Cementstone age, lie upon the teschenite a few yards east of the Crags and the teschenite here is locally cut by veins of dark tachylyte. To the south and east of this locality the sill splits up into a number of leaves separated by thin layers of intervening sediment.

Excursion B—Whinny Hill. 3 hours

The approach to Whinny Hill is most easily made from the western end of St Margaret's Loch which can be conveniently reached from either the Holyrood or Meadowbank Gates of the Holyrood Park.

11. Dasses Sill

The sill of the Dasses here forms a low westward facing cliff. Only a few feet in thickness, it consists of a highly altered Markle basalt transitional to mugearite. The top of the sill is well-exposed and shows a number of north-west—south-east corrugations, representing casts of drag-folds in the overlying sediments caused by the movement of the magma. A few inches of very slightly indurated sediment can be seen above the sill and directly below the turf at the eastern margin of the outcrop.

12. Long Row: Lava I

The Dunsapie basalt which forms Lava I is well-exposed at the northern termination of the Long Row. The base of the flow is not seen but the greater part of its thickness is exposed. The flow is sparsely vesicular throughout and the central part shows a crude columnar jointing. The irregular and slaggy top of the flow is exposed in the path leading to the Dry Dam almost where it joins the path uphill past St Anthony's Well; the irregularities in the top of the lava are filled with basaltic ash.

13. St Anthony's Well. Lower Ash of the Dry Dam

The Lower Ash of the Dry Dam is somewhat poorly exposed at this locality. A few feet above the top of Lava I there crops out a bed of white limestone, three feet in thickness. The limestone contains cherty nodules and is associated with dark sandy shales containing plant remains. In the small scrape on the south side of the path leading past St Anthony's Well, ashy and shaly beds are exposed and are overlain by another impure limestone. Lava 2, which overlies the Lower Ash, is not exposed at this locality on the south side of the St Anthony's Fault.

14. St Anthony's Well: Lava 2

This locality lies to the north of the path running to the east past St Anthony's Well and is the lowest westward facing cliff on the slope below St Anthony's Chapel. The well lies on the east-west St Anthony's Fault so that Locality 14 is separated from Localities 13 and 12 by this dislocation; the fault has thrown the rocks down to the north by some 75 ft. At Locality 14 Lava 2 crops out. The flow, of Craiglockhart basalt, is of no great thickness and is decomposed and vesicular throughout. At the south-western extremity of the exposure the flow has been gas-brecciated, the fragments now being cemented by calcite. The upper surface of Lava 2 is irregular, the irregularities being filled with ash or sediment.

15. Lava 2, Upper Ash of the Dry Dam.

This locality is protected by the Ministry of Works and no hammering is allowed. The upper surface of Lava 2 forms a small ledge in the westward facing cliff below St Anthony's Chapel. Above and to the east of the ledge the ash is exposed and is covered by the columnar basal portion of Lava 3. The ash, 4 ft. thick, is well-bedded and contains occasional volcanic bombs up to 2 ft. in diameter. Near its base the ash carries numerous coalified plant fragments; a tooth of *Rhizodus* and remains of *Elonichthys striatus* and *Callopristodus pectinatus* have been found here.

16. St. Anthony's Chapel: Lava 3

Lava 3 is a basalt of Craiglockhart type and the lower part, seen around the ruins of St Anthony's Chapel, is markedly columnar, the individual columns being about 2 ft. in diameter and inclined steeply to the west. Some 15 ft. above the base of the flow the markedly columnar portion grades into an irregularly columnar portion which is exposed locally at the base of the cliffs to the east of the Chapel. This, in turn, passes very gradually upwards into the topmost zone of the lava—an assemblage of basaltic blocks lying in a matrix of identical composition. The blocky portion has a marked pyroclastic appearance and most probably originated by the brecciation of the cold crust of the lava by the movement of the still liquid interior. The blocky portion is about 50 ft. thick. The total thickness of the flow exceeds 80 ft.

17. Pulpit Rock: Basalt Plug, Lavas 2, 4

The small parasitic vent of the Pulpit Rock is occupied by a plug of Craiglockhart basalt which forms a prominent cliff high on the eastern slopes of the Dry Dam. Columnar jointing is well-developed, the columns being curved; in the centre of the mass they are more or less vertical but, on being traced towards the margin, the individual columns approach the horizontal, indicating that they have been chilled against the vertical wall of the vent. To the south of the cliff the contact of the plug with Lava 2 is exposed, the lava being much altered in proximity to the junction. Lava 4, which to the south forms the cliff along the eastern wall of the Dry Dam, also comes into contact with the Pulpit Rock Vent but, being younger, naturally shows no increase of alteration at the contact. The connection between Lava 3 and its feeder—the plug in the Pulpit Rock Vent—is still preserved and may be traced on the north side of the vent.

18. Dry Dam: Upper Ash, Lavas 2, 4, 5, 6

At this locality the Upper Ash of the Dry Dam is exposed in a number of outcrops. Its base can be observed resting on Lava 2 and its top seen to be covered by Lava 4 which here forms the cliff immediately to the east of the Dry Dam. The ash here is coarse, especially in its upper part, and contains numerous ejected blocks and bombs of basalt.

Between Localities 18 and 19, Lavas 4, 5 and 6 can be examined. The foremost is a Dalmeny type basalt, the latter two are of Jedburgh type.

19. Whinny Hill Intrusion

Whinny Hill Intrusion, a small sill, lies between Lavas 6 and 7. The two flows are microporphyritic Jedburgh basalts and present a strong contrast in appearance to the markedly macroporphyritic Craiglockhart basalt of the sill. The sill lies along a hollow between the dip slope of Lava 6 to the west and the scarp of Lava 7 to the east. The feeding pipe of the intrusion cuts Lava 5, another Jedburgh basalt, 50 yd. to the south-west of the northern extremity of the sill outcrop.

20. Whinny Hill: Lavas 7, 8-10

The return route from Locality 19 lies at first eastwards across the dip slope of Whinny Hill. Here exposures of Lavas 7 (Jedburgh), 8, 9 and 10 (all Markle) can be seen. On reaching the Queen's Drive the road is followed northwards and westwards; roadside exposures of the same flows can be examined in descending order.

The Park can be left either at the Meadowbank or the Holyrood gates.

Excursion C—The Lion's Haunch and Head Vents. 3 hours

Access to the exposures to be examined can most conveniently be made by entering the Park by the Park Road Gate.

21. Queen's Drive: Samson's Ribs Crater Lavas

The Samson's Ribs crater lavas, exposed in the Queen's Drive, dip towards the centre of the Lion's Haunch Vent. The lowest flow is brecciated throughout and has a slaggy top overlain by a foot of red tuffaceous sandstone. Above comes another lava, again with a slaggy upper surface, and this is in turn succeeded by a third flow. Above this uppermost flow lies the main mass of crudely bedded agglomerate of the Lion's Haunch Vent.

22. Roche moutonnée, Glacial Striae

From the retaining wall on the north side of the Queen's Drive there protrudes a *roche moutonnée*. The rock is striated horizontally, the striations tending to narrow towards the east; some plucking of the eastern end of the mass has occurred. The direction and narrowing of the striations, and the plucking, all point to the existence of a stream of ice moving from west to east through the hollow now occupied by the Queen's Drive. A few yards to the east a slickensided surface occurs by the roadside and can be contrasted with the glaciated surface.

23 and 24. Samson's Ribs Intrusion, Agglomerate

A small exposure of columnar Dunsapie basalt occurs on the north side of the Queen's Drive above the retaining wall. The columns, a few inches across, plunge southwards. The exposure marks the north-eastern termination of the Samson's Ribs Intrusion, which here cuts the agglomerate overlying the Samson's Ribs crater lavas farther to the west. The main part of the intrusion, which is markedly columnar in nature, is best seen in the cliff below the Queen's Drive.

The north side of the Queen's Drive is here (24) marked by a cliff of coarse agglomerate containing abundant basalt blocks and a lesser proportion of blocks of sedimentary rocks. The basalt blocks are of Dunsapie or Markle type. The matrix in which the blocks lie is a red decomposed basaltic ash.

25. Crater Lavas and Ash

In the cliff above the Queen's Drive a crater lava of Jedburgh basalt rests on a few feet of ashy sediment which, in turn, lie on agglomerate; the lava and sediment dip towards the north-east at a moderate angle. A small north-south fault repeats the slaggy top of the flow and its covering of agglomerate. Approximately 100 yd. farther to the north-east, a crater of lava of mugearite is seen in the cliff above the Queen's Drive. This flow is covered by ashy sediments which are themselves overlain by agglomerate; the dip of the flow is again towards the north-east. Several small north-south faults cut this mugearite flow.

26. Loch Crag: Vent Margin, Lava I, Limestone

The southern margin of the Lion's Haunch Vent is exposed above the retaining wall of the Queen's Drive where it can be seen truncating Lava 1 and the sediments and ashes above and below that flow. The lava forms a low southward facing cliff which can be followed upwards for a short distance from the road until it is cut across by the vent. The actual contact is not seen but can be fixed to within a foot or two. At this point the feeder of the Lion's Haunch Basalt occurs at the vent wall so that the contact is between the sparsely porphyritic Dunsapie basalt of the lava and the highly porphyritic Dunsapie basalt of the feeder. Sediments of the Cementstone Group have been seen below the lava; they are truncated by the vent and lie against agglomerate. Above the lava ash and sediments are visible; they are cut across by the vent which here also contains agglomerate. Blocks of a white limestone, identical to a bed seen *in situ* some feet above the lava, are found sparsely throughout the agglomerates at this locality.

27. Dunsapie Hill: Intrusion, Mugearite Lava

To the east of Dunsapie Hill, a mugearite lava forms a number of small outcrops. The rock is pale purplish-grey and is cut by numerous platy joints. It lies above a Markle flow exposed farther to the south. Both flows are cut by the Dunsapie Hill Intrusion within the Lion's Haunch Vent.

28. Lion's Haunch Basalt

The highly-porphyritic Lion's Haunch Basalt, the remains of a lava-lake resting on the agglomerate which forms the chief infilling of the Lion's Haunch Vent, is well-seen in numerous exposures at this locality.

29. Lion's Head Basalt, Viewpoint

The summit of Arthur's Seat—the Lion's Head—is formed of a glacially moulded basaltic plug which acted as the feeder for Lava 4 and which, on consolidation, blocked the Lion's Head Vent. From the summit the chief geological features of the Lothians and Fife can be clearly seen.

30 and 31. Lion's Head Vent Margin, Agglomerate

This locality lies at the junction of the Lion's Head Vent and Lava 1. On tracing the lava southwards, it becomes shattered and altered close to the vent and its dip increases from less than 20° to 40°. The actual contact is not visible, but its position can be fixed within a few feet. A dyke of Craiglockhart basalt, the feed of Lava 2, lies within the vent at the junction. On the slope above the dyke the fine agglomerate of the vent is exposed.

The agglomerate of the Lion's Head Vent is roughly bedded and has an inwards dip (31). It contains numerous small fragments of Dunsapie and Craiglockhart basalt but no fragments of Markle basalt occur. The small size of the fragments and the absence of Markle blocks distinguish this agglomerate from that of the Lion's Head Vent. A large gully, known as the Gutted Haddie, has been eroded along the line of contact between the Lion's Head and the Lion's Haunch vents; some 50 yd. to the north of this gully a small basalt dyke cuts the Lion's Head Vent.

The return from this excursion can be made either by the Hunter's Bog to the Holyrood Gate or through the low col between the Salisbury Crags and the Lion's Haunch to the Park Road Gate.

REFERENCES

BLACK, G. P. *The Geology of Arthur's Seat.* Oliver and Boyd. Edinburgh. *In press.*

CLARK, R. H. 1956. A petrological study of the Arthur's Seat Volcano. *Trans. Roy. Soc. Edin.*, vol. 63, pp. 37–70.

DAY, T. C. 1933. *Arthur's Seat: a Ruined Volcano*. Oliver and Boyd. Edinburgh.

PEACH, B. N. 1921. Description of the Arthur's Seat Volcano. *Mem. Geol. Surv.*

G. P. BLACK

JOPPA SHORE

O.S. One-inch Map, Seventh Series, Sheet 62
G.S. One-inch Map, Sheet 32 (Scotland)
Route-map p. 46

＊

IT is important to note that this excursion should be undertaken when the tide is low, as most of the rocks are completely covered at high water; it will also be found that, from time to time, some of the softer beds are obscured by sand and mud.

The strata exposed on the shore at Joppa provide an excellent section of the upper part of the Upper Limestone Group, almost the whole of the Passage Group (formerly known as the Roslin Sandstone Group) and the lower part of the Productive Coal Measures. All the beds belong to the Upper Carboniferous. The Upper Limestone Group and probably part of the Passage Group were deposited during the Upper *Eumorphoceras* Age (E_2); strata of the *Homoceras* (H), Lower *Reticuloceras* (R_1) and Upper *Reticuloceras* (R_2) ages, as well as part at least of the succeeding *Gastrioceras* (G) Age, appear to be absent, the indications being that an unconformity occurs in this part of the succession in Scotland. The presence of a break in the sequence of floras of the 'Roslin Sandstone', generally known as the 'plant-break', has long been known (Kidston 1894, 1923; Crookall, 1939; Clough and Gibson *in* Peach *et al.*, 1910, p. 244). It is difficult to define this break in the Passage Group, but nevertheless it seems at least likely that the upper part of the Group, above the

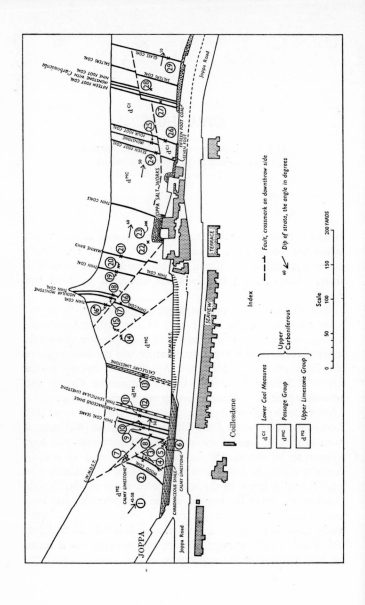

Index

d^Cl	Lower Coal Measures
d^MC	Passage Group
d^M2	Upper Limestone Group

Upper Carboniferous

---ᵀ--- Fault, crossmark on downthrow side

↙60 Dip of strata, the angle in degrees

Scale

0   50   100   150   200 YARDS

plant-break, will eventually be found to belong rather to the Productive Coal Measures than to the Millstone Grit as defined in the Pennine region of England.

Most of the Productive Coal Measures exposed on the shore at Joppa probably fall within the *Carbonicola communis* Zone of the non-marine lamellibranch sequence.

The strata lie on the western limb of the main syncline of the Midlothian Coalfield, the dips ranging from 45° to 60° towards the east.

Many of the thicker coal seams formerly exposed were worked at the crop, and the positions of the outcrops are now marked by sand-filled gaps in the succession.

Joppa shore is conveniently reached by Corporation bus from the centre of Edinburgh. Alight at Esplanade Terrace and proceed eastwards along the shore, visiting the localities in the following order:

(1) *Sandstone below the Wood Coal.* The massive sandstone which crops out north of the children's paddling pool lies below the Wood Coal.

(2) *The Wood Coal.* The outcrop of this seam is now obscured by sand and mud.

(3) *Carbonaceous shale.* About 14 yd. to the east there is an outcrop of pale seatclay, overlain by a bed of hard dark carbonaceous shale, about 6 ft. thick; the shale contains ferruginous ribs and nodules, and both shale and ironstone contain fish-remains.

(4) *Edmondia punctatella band.* The bituminous shale at locality 3 is overlain by 1 ft. of soft crushed shale, succeeded by 11 ft. of grey shale containing *Lingula mytilloides*, *Actinopteria ?* cf. *persulcata* (McCoy), *Edmondia punctatella*, and *Sanguinolites* cf. *clavatus*. *E. punctatella* is numerous in a band about 3 ft. from the base. The latter fossil occurs below the Calmy Limestone in many parts of the Midland Valley of Scotland; it is not, however, confined to this horizon, but has also been found underneath the Orchard Limestone (Wilson, 1958, p. 21).

(5) *Marine shell-bed.* Another bed of dark-grey fossiliferous shale, 5 ft. thick, lies about 50 ft. higher in the succession; *Conchotrema sp.*, *Lingula mytilloides*, *Cardiomorpha* cf. *limosa* (Fleming), *Prothyris* cf. *elegans*, three species of *Sanguinolites*, and *Bucanopsis sp.* have been found in this bed.

(6) *Calmy Limestone.* This limestone lies about 6 ft. higher in the succession, and crops out on the foreshore near the base of the sea-wall, the details being: limestone, grey with reddish veins, with crinoid columnals, *Productus* (*Gigantoproductus*) cf. *latissimus*, *P.* (*Sinuatella*) *sp.*, and *Spirifer sp.*, 1 ft.; shale 6 in.; on limestone 2 ft. 9 in.

(7) *Calmy Limestone displaced by fault.* Just north of locality 6 the limestone is cut off by a fault and is displaced about 60 yd. to the north-west; the section of the limestone on the north side of the fault is: limestone, grey, impure, 2 in.; sandy shale, grey, limy, 2 in.; limestone, grey, impure, 6 in.; sandy shale, grey, limy, 5 in.; limestone, grey, 1 ft. 9 in. There is a gap in the succession immediately above this exposure of the Calmy Limestone, probably occupied by a fault.

The beds between the Calmy Limestone and the Castlecary Limestone include sandstones, shales, seatclays, and thin coal-seams, and an interesting feature is the occurrence of several *Lingula* bands and marine shell-beds in the central or upper part of the succession. These fossiliferous horizons correspond to the Plean Limestones of the Central Coalfield of Scotland.

(8) *Lingula band.* The lowest of the *Lingula* bands is to be found on the north side of the north-west-trending fault which displaces the Calmy Limestone. Here *Lingula mytilloides* is found in the hard dark shale overlying a 3-in. coal with seatclay ribs.

(9) *Lingula band and marine shell-bed.* About 9 yd. to the east a coal, up to 1 ft. thick, crops out, overlain by 6 in. of dark pyritised shale containing *Lingula*, succeeded by 4 ft. 6 in. of shale containing ? *Edmondia sulcata*, *Nuculana attenuata*, and ? *Sedgwickia suborbicularis* Hind.

(10) *Lingula band. Lingula* cf. *mytilloides* and fish-remains are

present in a bed of shale with thin ironstone ribs overlying a 5-in. coal about 9 ft. 6 in. higher in the succession.

(11) *Anthraconauta band.* About 7 yd. to the east another thin coal is present, overlain by soft shale containing *Anthraconauta.*

(12) *Marine band.* The next marine band, the most fossiliferous in this part of the succession, is to be found 4 yd. farther east, and consists of about 12 ft. of soft grey shale with ironstone ribs and nodules; a lenticular impure limestone about $1\frac{1}{2}$ in. thick occurs 2 ft. 6 in. from the top of the bed, and the fossils are most numerous just above this limestone. The fauna includes a Fenestellid, *Orbiculoidea sp.*, *Productus* (*Dictyoclostus*) aff. *muricatus*, *P.* (*Dictyoclostus*) *pugilis*, *Schellwienella sp.*, *Parallelodon semicostatus* ?, *Schizodus* cf. *triangularis* Hind, *Sulcatopinna flabelliformis*, and *Bucanopsis sp.* *Lingula mytilloides* has been found in a bed of shale about 11 ft. above the lenticular limestone.

The interval from here to the Castlecary Limestone is occupied mainly by thick sandstones, with beds of seatclay in the upper part.

(13) *Castlecary Limestone.* This limestone is well exposed on the foreshore at Joppa, the details being: limestone, dark, earthy, 1 in.; sandy shale, limy, shelly and crinoidal, 2 in.; limestone, blue and brown, with solution cavities 5 ft.; shale, grey, shelly, 4 ft. 6 in., on limestone, grey and brown, shelly and crinoidal, about 3 ft.

The Castlecary Limestone is overlain by a bed of dark-grey carbonaceous shale about 3 ft. thick, containing abundant *Anthraconauta sp.*, with ostracods and fish-remains; this shale probably represents the oil-shale which overlies the Levenseat Limestone in the eastern part of the Central Coalfield. Beds of sandstone and seatclay follow the shale, then there is a gap in the succession, the foreshore being covered with mud and boulders.

(14) *Ironstone with Lingula.* On the east side of the above-mentioned gap an ironstone, about $1\frac{1}{2}$ in. thick, containing

Lingula fragments, can be seen, underlain by soft grey shale with occasional marine fossils.

(15) *Fault and marine band*. A north-west trending fault crosses the shore between localities 14 and 15, where a bed of dark shale, 1 ft. 6 in. thick, containing *Lingula* and occasional marine shells crops out.

(16) *Marine shell-bed*. About 38 yd. to the south-east, at the top of a thick sandstone, there is a seatclay 1 ft. 3 in. thick, overlain by 6 in. of coaly shale and coal, succeeded by dark shale containing occasional Productid fragments. A small fault displaces this shell-bed a few yards to the north-west (16A).

(17) *Marine shell-bed*. The details of the section here are: dark shale with *Lingula, Productus, Edmondia, Palæolima, Euphemites*, and an orthocone nautiloid.

(18) *Thin coal, and shale with gastropods*. A few yards to the east a thin coal may be seen, resting on 2 in. of seatclay, which is underlain by an irregular lenticular rooty sandstone. The coal rib is overlain by 4 in. of sandy shale containing gastropods.

(19) *Marine shell-bed*. About 33 yd. to the east, a bed of shale just over 4 ft. thick, with small fossiliferous ironstone nodules, crops out; *Productus* and a poorly preserved coral have been found here.

(20) *Shale with Lingula and Productus*. About 6 ft. of seatclay overlie the shell-bed at locality 19, succeeded by 6 in. of coal, 2 ft. 4 in. of shale and 5 ft. of seatclay. These beds are overlain in turn by about 3 ft. of dark shale, in which *Lingula* and fragments of *Productus* have been found.

(21) *Lingula band and marine shell-bed*. Some 12 yd. to the east a pale-grey red-mottled gritty seatclay, 2 ft. 9 in. thick, will be observed, overlain by about 2 ft. of sandstone containing roots. A bed of shale 6 ft. 3 in. thick rests on this sandstone; *Lingula*, fish-remains, and plant-remains occur at the base of the shale. Fragments of marine shells have been found about 2 ft. 6 in. from the base of the shale, and also in an ironstone

rib which lies near the top; the fauna includes *Orbiculoidea*, Orthotetid fragments, and *Productus*.

For the next 70 yd. horizontally the strata are composed principally of red, grey and yellow mottled mudstones, sandy in parts, with argillaceous sandstone bands; thin coal seams are present in the upper part.

(22) *Stigmaria*. Several *Stigmaria* preserved in ironstone can be seen north-west of Joppa Salt Works.

(23) *Megaspores*. About 30 yd. to the east of locality 22 there is a pale siliceous rib ½ in. to 1 in. thick which contains numerous megaspores.

The upper part of the Passage Group consists mainly of reddish current-bedded sandstone, pebbly in places, with beds of mudstone.

(24) *Seven Foot Coal*. In the northern part of the Midlothian Coalfield the base of the Productive Coal Measures is taken at the base of the Seven Foot Coal. On the shore at Joppa only the lower and upper parts of this seam are now visible, but according to old records the section formerly seen was: coal 1 ft. 3 in.; fireclay 4 ft.; coal 6 ft.; fireclay 2 ft. 6 in., on coal 2 ft.

(25) *Naiadites band*. The strata between the Seven Foot Coal and the Pinkie Four Foot Coal consist mainly of sandy shale, shale and seatclay, the total thickness being 35 ft. About 12 ft. above the Seven Foot Coal there is a bed, approximately 1 ft. thick, consisting of alternations of sandy ironstone and coaly shale, which has yielded *Naiadites*.

(26) *Musselband in beds above the Four Foot Coal*. A gap of about 4 ft. represents the position of the Pinkie Four Foot Coal, and the details of the strata above the seam are as follows:

	ft.	in.
Shale, soft, grey, with *Anthracosphærium* ? and *Carbonicola sp.*; thin ironstone ribs - - -	1	6
Shale, hard, dark, carbonaceous, with fish-remains	1	6

Ironstone, hard, dark-grey, sandy   -   -   -   0   1

Shale and sandy shale, dark; in places there is an
    irregular nodular ironstone rib about 1 in. thick
    at the top of this item, containing *Carbonicola*   -   0   7

Seatclay and coaly seatclay -   -   -   -   -   1   5+

Position of Pinkie Four Foot Coal

(27) *Musselbands above the Fifteen Foot Coal.* The interval between the strata described above and the position of the Fifteen
Foot Coal is occupied mainly by a massive current-bedded
sandstone, coarse and gritty in parts, the total thickness of
measures from the top of the Pinkie Four Foot Coal to the
base of the Fifteen Foot Coal being about 92 ft.

The Fifteen Foot Coal, now totally obscured at Joppa, is
said to have been 12 ft. 6 in. thick at that locality. The beds
between the Fifteen Foot and Nine Foot coals are:

	ft.	in.
Position of Nine Foot Coal		
Seatclay, sandstone and shale - - - -	5	10
Shale with crushed mussels - - - -	0	6
Ironstone, nodular, with numerous *Carbonicola* -	0	3
Shale with numerous crushed shells; the fauna includes *Spirorbis sp.*, *Anthraconauta* cf. *subovata*, *A.* aff. *trapeziforma* Dewar, *Carbonicola* aff. *communis* Davies and Trueman, *C. sp.* intermediate between *pseudorobusta* and *rhomboidalis* Hind, *C. sp.* intermediate between *communis* and *martini* Trueman and Weir, and *C. sp.* - - - - - - -	0	7
Sandy shale and sandstone - - - -	10	10
Shale with thin sandy ironstone ribs - - -	4	0
Shale with a 1-in. nodular ironstone rib containing *Carbonicola* aff. *communis* - - -	1	0+
Position of Fifteen Foot Coal		

The section of the Nine Foot Coal formerly seen on the

shore at Joppa was: coal 1 ft. 1 in.; fireclay 2 ft., on coal 5 ft. 6 in.

(28) *Beds above Nine Foot Coal.* The beds between the Nine Foot Coal and Salters Coal consist of 33 ft. of rapidly alternating sandstone, sandy shale and shale, with some seatclays. About 8 ft. above the Nine Foot Coal there are two thin shale bands, 6 in. apart, containing *Spirorbis sp.*, *Anthraconauta* cf. *tenuioides* Dewar, and *A. sp.*

Salters Coal, when exposed, occurred in two leaves: coal 2 ft.; fireclay 4 ft.; coal 2 ft., but a sand-filled gap now marks the position of the outcrop.

The strata between the Salters and Glass coals are composed almost entirely of sandstone, with a thin shale band in the middle, containing plant fossils.

(29) *Beds above the Glass Coal.* A gap of 4 ft. 6 in. represents the position of the outcrop of the Glass Coal; on the east side of the gap 10 in. of hard dark carbonaceous sandy shale with fish-remains are exposed, succeeded by 2 ft. 4 in. of reddish-purple shale containing occasional small mussels.

The remainder of the section consists mainly of massive reddish-purple current-bedded sandstone.

REFERENCES

CROOKALL, R., 1939. The Plant 'Break' in the Carboniferous Rocks of Great Britain. *Bull. Geol. Surv. Gt. Brit.*, No. 1, pp. 13–26.

KIDSTON, R., 1894. On the Various Divisions of the British Carboniferous Rocks as determined by their Fossil Flora. *Proc. Roy. Phys. Soc. Edin.*, vol. 12, pp. 183–257.

——1923. Fossil Plants of the Carboniferous Rocks of Great Britain. *Mem. Geol. Surv., Palæont.*

PEACH, B. N., *et al.*, 1910. The Geology of the Neighbourhood of Edinburgh. 2nd. edit. *Mem. Geol. Surv.*

TULLOCH, W. and WALTON, H. S., 1958. The Geology of the Midlothian Coalfield. *Mem. Geol. Surv.*

WILSON, R. B., 1958. A Revision of the Carboniferous Lamellibranchs *Edmondia punctatella* (Jones) and *'Estheria'*
youngii Jones. *Bull. Geol. Surv. Gt. Brit.*, No. 15, pp.
21–28.

W. TULLOCH

GOSFORD BAY—ABERLADY POINT

O.S. One-inch Map, Sheet 62
G.S. One-inch Map, Sheet 33
Route-map p. 56

—

THIS excursion is intended primarily to illustrate the rhythmic pattern of some of the sediments of the Lower Limestone Group which are well exposed between Craigielaw Point and Aberlady Point. On the way to Aberlady, however, the opportunity can be taken to examine a portion of the '25-ft.' raised beach and a dolerite sill of Permo-Carboniferous age at the southern end of Gosford Bay. The walking distance involved is about 3 to 4 miles and the excursion, which should be done at low tide, takes about half a day. The journey from Edinburgh may be made by bus (S.M.T. to North Berwick) to the southern end of Gosford Bay or by car on the A.198 road.

After leaving Longniddry and joining the Port Seton road at the coast, stop at the second official parking place past the road junction.

I. Gosford Bay: Raised Beach (Not shown on route-map)

The first locality is on the shore below bushes at the point where the broad sweep of Gosford Bay first comes into view (444778). A small cliff about 12 to 15 ft. high shows a section of sandstone underlain by about 10 ft. of interbedded black micaceous carbonaceous shales (with plant fragments) and thin fine-grained sandstone bands with well developed ripple marks. The beds dip between 15° and 20° towards the east and

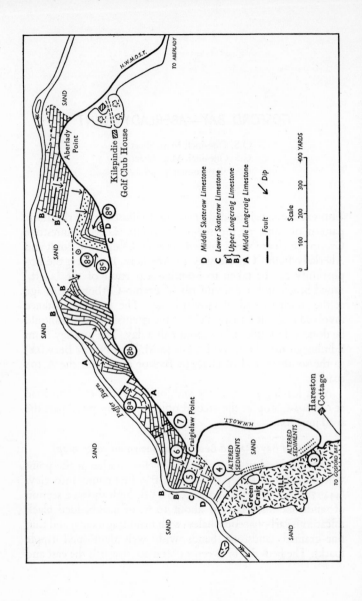

Scale

0   100   200   300   400 YARDS

D *Middle Skateraw Limestone*
C *Lower Skateraw Limestone*
B'} *Upper Longcraig Limestone*
B } *Middle Longcraig Limestone*
A *Middle Longcraig Limestone*

— Fault

↙ *Dip*

form part of the south-western limb of the Gosford Bay syncline. On top of these beds can be seen up to 5 ft. of raised beach deposits containing numerous shells (*Ostrea, Patella, Littorina, Dentalium*) and shell fragments along with blocks of dolerite of local origin. Foraminifera and ostracods are present in the sandy matrix.

2. Gosford Bay Sill, South (Not shown on route-map)

At the seaward end of the above exposure baked shale is seen to be underlain by 'white trap'—the altered top of the Gosford Bay olivine-analcite-dolerite sill. ('White trap' is formed by the action, on the already crystallised rock-forming silicates, of CO_2 and other organic gases driven out of carbonaceous sediments by heat, and consists of the carbonates of lime, magnesium and iron with kaolin and muscovite.) The contact can be traced a considerable distance seawards.

Prominent sheet-jointing in the dolerite can be seen parallel to the dip near the contact, but south-westwards the joint-surfaces dip in the opposite direction, presumably indicating a change of attitude of the contact surface. The dolerite contains veinlets of calcite and quartz (in places amethystine) and patches of white trap are conspicuous. A large block of sandstone can be seen in the dolerite near the high-water mark about 25 yd. from the contact. North-east of the contact, in Gosford Bay, outcrops are poor but sandstone and shale can be seen in places.

3. Gosford Bay Sill, North (route-map)

About 200 yd. past the North Lodge gates of Gosford House take the footpath northwards along the shore for about half a mile, noting the outcrops of dolerite on the shore. Just past the golf course green, west of Hareston Cottage, the base of the sill is reached. Here the dip of the sediments is towards the south-west as we are now on the north-eastern limb of the Gosford Bay syncline. The contact is not visible but baked sandstone can be seen within a foot or two of it.

Outcrops of undulating beds of sandstone and shale appear through the sand a few yards north-east of the contact. Dolerite and white trap are also visible, probably indicating the presence of a thin offshoot below the main sill.

Walk across the large expanse of sand to the north-west, keeping to the east of Green Craig where the contact of the sill and sediments can be located to within a foot or two. The line of contact can be followed to the Peffer Burn, west of Craigielaw Point, and again an isolated outcrop to the east and below the main contact shows altered sediments.

4. Middle Skateraw Limestone (D)

About 50 yd. north-east, across the intervening sand, the dip slope of a well-jointed limestone (D) is visible. The surface is undulating slightly but in general the dip is about 15° to the south-south-west. The limestone is a hard massive dark-grey bed about 12 ft. in thickness. It contains crinoid fragments and Productid brachiopods. Immediately below the overhanging limestone is a dark-grey mudstone which has been extensively bored by present-day molluscs.

5. Lower Skateraw Limestone (C)

The beds below limestone D are poorly exposed but at a distance of about 30 yd. the next limestone (C) is seen. This well-jointed limestone is between 2 and 4 ft. in thickness and is a hard grey rock also containing crinoids and brachiopods. Careful search below the overhanging limestone shows about an inch of mudstone underlain by an inch or two of coal. This coal is followed downwards by a seatearth, sandy shale and sandstone and about 30 yd. north-east of the limestone a conspicuous false-bedded and ripple-marked sandstone crops out.

6. Upper Longcraig Limestone (B′, B)

Below the false-bedded sandstone there is shale, flaggy limestone (B′) and then a pale-brown limestone (B) with a nodular or 'rubbly' top surface. This limestone is dolomitic and contains many crinoid fragments. It forms a prominent scarp about 12 ft. high which continues seawards to form the Long Craig. There has been considerable undercutting of the soft shale and coal below this limestone. In places the coal reaches 10 in. in thickness and it is underlain by a seatearth.

7. Middle Longcraig Limestone (A) and Faults

Towards the east for a few yards there are many fallen blocks of limestone B before the lowest limestone (A) is seen. This is a particularly easy limestone to recognize; it is yellow-brown in colour and is made up largely of colonies of *Lithostrotion junceum* and *L. pauciradiale*. A field-name such as 'spaghetti-' or 'macaroni-rock' suggests itself immediately (cf. Catcraig, p. 100). The limestone is extremely fossiliferous containing, as well as compound corals, genera such as *Caninia* and *Zaphrentis*, and the brachiopods *Productus, Spirifer, Avonia, Pustula, Composita* and *Rhynchonella*.

When traced towards high-water mark (H.W.M.) the scarp of limestone B is seen to end abruptly and immediately below it can be seen limestone A. Higher up on the bank, just below the grass, the 'rubbly' limestone B can be seen again where it continues eastwards for about 20 yd. before it is thrown down again to beach level.

Two small north-westerly trending faults throwing up the strata between them cause this displacement of the outcrops. The effect can best be seen from the seaward end of the upthrown block.

8. Anticline and Succession to Aberlady Point

Limestone A can be followed eastwards along the shore, its dip decreasing until the crest of an anticline is reached (8a). Below the limestone are sandstone and shales while in places thin (2 to 3 in.) sandstone dykes can be seen cutting the limestone.

About 80 yd. east of the crest of the anticline the now easterly dipping limestone is faulted and its base thrown up to near H.W.M. Keeping to H.W.M. limestone B can once again be identified because of its characteristic appearance (8b). The bed can be followed along the shore to just below the octagonal blockhouse where it swings out to sea. The dip in this area is slight and the outcrop of the soft beds between limestones A and B has widened considerably.

Above limestone B is the flaggy upper portion B' and above it, about 50 yd. east of the blockhouse at H.W.M., raised-beach deposits can be seen. Continuing along H.W.M. a small cliff is reached exposing irregularly interbanded shale and sandstone (8c). The shale forming a wave-cut platform at the base of this cliff contains Productids and crinoids. Near the red-tiled cottage a false-bedded sandstone (cf. 5) is found at the top of the cliff. Farther east this sandstone can be seen swinging seawards and there is a small stack (the 'King's Kist') formed of an outlier of the sandstone which rests on undercut shales below.

Eastwards and landwards of the 'King's Kist' the small-scale folding is rather complex but in general the beds are in the form of a syncline (8e) and limestones C and D and the false-bedded sandstone can be located. West and east of Aberlady Point an extensive outcrop of limestone B (below less obvious limestone B') is prominent, the dip being about 5° to the south.

From here along the shore it is about a mile to Aberlady although if private transport has been used it is quicker to return along the shore to the footpath from Gosford Bay.

REFERENCES

CLOUGH, C. T., *et al.*, 1910. The Geology of East Lothian. *Mem. Geol. Surv.*

P. McL. D. DUFF

GARLETON HILLS and TRAPRAIN LAW

O.S. One-inch Map, Seventh Series, Sheets 62 and 63
G.S. One-inch Map, Sheet 33 (Scotland)
Route-map p. 62

✦

THE main objects of this excursion are to see typical examples of the Lower Carboniferous trachytic volcanic rocks of East Lothian, and some of the associated basalts and mugearites. The route is chosen so as to illustrate the geological structure of the area. Incidentally attention is directed to a hæmatite vein, to a Permo-Carboniferous quartz-dolerite dyke, and to the effects of glaciation. To cover the area in a short time motor transport is essential.

The volcanic area is of particular interest for the following reasons: (1) here F. H. Hatch (1892) initiated petrological description of Scottish Carboniferous igneous rocks on modern lines; (2) Hatch recognized the alkaline character of the rocks and the presence of nepheline in the Traprain Law intrusion; he thus proved the existence of volcanic rocks of Palæozoic age, essentially similar in character to alkaline rocks of modern volcanic districts. As a result Rosenbusch, the great German petrographer, was convinced that the Continental age-classification of volcanic rocks was artificial and misleading.

Volcanic rocks occupy an area of about 50 square miles in East Lothian. The volcanic group is intercalated in sedimentary strata belonging to the Calciferous Sandstone Measures and, broadly speaking, all these rocks have a gentle westerly dip. An anticlinal area near North Berwick is, however, marked by a core of sedimentary rocks.

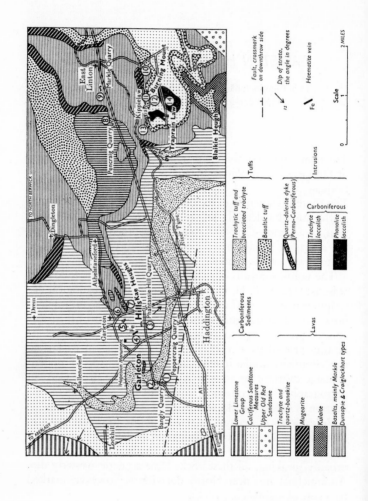

Carboniferous Sediments
- Lower Limestone Group
- Calciferous Sandstone Measures
- Upper Old Red Sandstone

Lavas
- Trachyte and quartz-banakite
- Mugearite
- Kulaite
- Basalts, mainly Markle Dunsapie & Craiglockhart types

Tuffs
- Trachytic tuff and brecciated trachyte
- Basaltic tuff

Intrusions
- Quartz-dolerite dyke (Permo-Carboniferous)
- Trachyte laccolith
- Phonolite laccolith

Fault, crossmark on downthrow side

15 ⟋ Dip of strata, the angle in degrees

Fe ▬ Haematite vein

Scale

0 ————————— 1 ————————— 2 MILES

The district as a whole is one of low relief, but the trachytic rocks locally form relatively high ground (Garleton Hills, 590 ft.; Traprain Law, 724 ft.).

The stratigraphical sequence may be summarized as follows:

7. Sediments of Lower Limestone Group of Carboniferous Limestone Series.
6. Sediments of Calciferous Sandstone Measures.
5. Marl and volcanic detritus of Calciferous Sandstone Measures.

Local Unconformity

4. Trachytic lavas (with interbedded trachytic tuff north and north-west of Haddington).
3. Basalt lavas of Markle, Dunsapie and Craiglockhart types, with intercalated flows of mugearite and, south of Traprain Law, of kulaite.
2. Basaltic tuff, with some limestone.
1. Sediments of Calciferous Sandstone Measures.

During the eruption of the trachytic lavas, or very shortly afterwards, trachytic rocks were intruded in the form of stocks (North Berwick Law, and the Bass Rock off the adjacent coast: phonolitic trachyte) or laccoliths (Pencraig Wood: trachyte; Traprain Law: phonolite).

1. Bangly Quarry: Trachytic Lava

The visitor should leave the main Tranent-Haddington highway at the road junction 1½ miles beyond Gladsmuir and proceed northwards for a mile until Bangly Quarry (1) is seen on the east. This large disused quarry, nearly 80 ft. deep, has been excavated, near the top of the trachytic lava sequence, in quartz-banakite, a trachytic rock (trachyandesite) containing aegerine-augite, numerous small phenocrysts of plagioclase and some of orthoclase. At the east end of the quarry, in the south face, the banakite, here fairly fresh, is cut by a 12-ft.

north and south dyke, conspicuous because of its cross-jointing; the chilled margin is clearly seen on the west side. The dyke is rather decomposed but appears to be a trachy-basalt, and contains large crystals of plagioclase and orthoclase. During the quarrying of the banakite many orthoclase pheno-crysts up to 5 cm. in length are said to have been found locally. There is little doubt, however, as T. C. Day has suggested, that these specimens came from the dyke, not the banakite.

2. Bangly Braehead: Trachytic Tuff in Lavas

A quarter of a mile north of Bangly Quarry, at Bangly Braehead road junction (2), one of two small quarries on the west of the road should now be visited. The quarries are excavated in a belt of trachytic tuff intercalated in the trachytic lavas. The accessible exposure is a brecciated and xenolithic trachyte, representing the top of a lava flow. True tuff, however, occurs in association with similar rock at Abbey Quarry, north-east of Haddington.

3. Phantassie Hill: Trachyte Lava

The route now follows the road eastwards for a mile to the Smithy Cottage at a cross-roads on the Haddington-Aberlady road. From this point the visitor must proceed on foot, along a lane leading eastwards, and leave it when the rocky knolls of Phantassie are seen on the north through a gateway in the hedge. Phantassie Hill (3) is formed of a fine-grained trachyte lava, with conspicuous sanidine phenocrysts; particularly fresh specimens may be obtained in the uppermost of two disused quarries.

4. Garleton Hæmatite Mine

The route now leads north-westwards to the long abandoned Garleton Hæmatite Mine (4), surrounded by fencing and stone walls. Here, at an old day-level, strings of kidney-ore may be seen cutting brecciated trachyte. The vein, which runs for a short distance north-north-westwards along a crush-belt, was 3 ft. to 6 ft. in width and produced 10,000 tons of ore in the year 1874.

5. Skid Hill: Trachytic Lava

From this point the route runs across country for 500 yd. to the large road-metal quarry in the quartz-banakite lava of Skid Hill (5). The rock is similar to that of Bangly Quarry and contains numerous small feldspar phenocrysts showing interesting corrosion-phenomena. The road-metal quarry, about 70 ft. deep, is excavated in solid banakite.

6. Viewpoint, south of Garleton

On reaching the Drem-Haddington road (6) to the east of the quarry a good view is obtained of a hollow, floored by basalt lavas, leading east-north-eastwards towards Athelstaneford. The great Kae Heughs trachyte scarp rising abruptly to the south shows clearly that the trachytic lavas of the Garleton Hills overlie the basalts that form the lower ground on the north.

7. Kae Heughs: Mugearite, Basalt and Quartz-dolerite

A visit may profitably be paid to a flow of mugearite intercalated in the basalts immediately below the Kae Heughs scarp, and to a typical Permo-Carboniferous quartz-dolerite dyke, which is well seen about 100 yd. from the road (7).

8. Pencraig Wood: Trachyte Laccolith

The visitor should now proceed southwards and then east-north-eastwards along the Haddington-East Linton road to the quarry on the north of the road at Pencraig Wood (8), where the sparsely porphyritic trachyte of the Pencraig laccolith is seen. This much-decomposed rock has been used for road-bottoming.

F

9. Markle Quarry: Markle type Basalt

Three-quarters of a mile nearer East Linton, Markle Quarry is seen on the north of the road, and about 150 yd. from it. This large disused quarry (9) is the type locality of basalt of Markle type, crowded with phenocrysts of plagioclase feldspar. The quarry face is about 25 ft. high and, near the top, at the south end, the rock becomes amygdaloidal and the feldspar phenocrysts sparse. The basalt is considerably decomposed throughout.

10. Viewpoint near Traprain Farm

The route now runs through East Linton, where Markle basalt has been used as a building stone, across the River Tyne, with its extensive outcrops of basalt lava laid bare in a valley that has been overdeepened by late-Glacial melt-waters, and southwards across the basalts exposed along the road to Traprain Farm. From the fork at this farm the visitor should follow for 200 yd. the road leading to Kippielaw Farm and enter the field on the south of the road (10). The view from this point is of great interest. To the west and north, beyond the Tyne valley, can be seen the high ground formed by the trachytic rocks of the Garleton Hills and Pencraig Wood, with the basalts of the Markle Quarry area to the east. North Berwick Law, the Bass Rock, and the Isle of May (a teschenite sill) are seen in the distance. To the south the resistant mass of the Traprain Law laccolith rises abruptly above the soft sedimentary rocks which surround it. The Law shows 'crag and tail' form. If private transport is used it can now be sent direct to Traprain Law Quarry to await the party.

11. Kippielaw Area: Mugearite and Basalt Lavas

From the viewpoint the route now follows a scarp formed by a small outlier of reddish mugearite, with typical close-set platy jointing. Just before a stone wall is reached fragments of the slaggy top of the mugearite may be seen in the field just north of the scarp. After crossing the wall by a stile, another wall should be followed in a west-south-westerly direction until Kippielaw Quarry (11) is reached, just south-east of the farm. This old quarry is excavated in one of the basalt lava flows below the mugearite and close to the base of the volcanic sequence. The rock of Kippielaw Quarry is an olivine-basalt of Dunsapie type, with conspicuous phenocrysts of feldspar, augite and olivine. The road north of Kippielaw should now be joined at the cottages to the east of the farm buildings. A glacial groove trending E. 15° N. is preserved on basalt lava just in front of the cottages.

12. Kippielaw Farm to Traprain Law: Calciferous Sandstone Sediments and Volcanic Rocks

From the north-west corner of Kippielaw Farm a wall trending a little south of west should now be followed for 250 yd., and then an abrupt turn made southwards along another wall leading towards the stone-breaking plant of Traprain Law road-metal quarry. This route gives a traverse at right angles to the strike and takes the visitor down in the succession on to the Calciferous Sandstone sediments underlying the lavas (12). In the immediate vicinity there are no satisfactory exposures of the basaltic ash and associated limestone that characterize the base of the volcanic sequence north-east and south-east of Traprain Law. Typical sediments of the underlying Calciferous Sandstone Measures are, however, exposed at several places in the fields to the west of the wall. The steep northerly dip (45° to 70°) of the beds was produced by the intrusion of the Traprain Law phonolite laccolith. When the molten rock was intruded in this mushroom-like form it domed up the overlying sediments and lavas. In consequence, denudation has now exposed around the Law an inner ring of sediments and an outer (incomplete) ring of lavas, dipping away from the central intrusive mass.

13. Burning Mount and Hairy Craig: Basalt Plug and Phonolite Sheet, Dry Valley

As the traverse is made towards Traprain Law a small basalt plug or vent, known as the Burning Mount, is seen to the west, and beyond it the rocks of the Hairy Craig (13). The latter forms part of a vesicular sheet-like intrusion of phonolite on the northern flank of the laccolith.

Between the Burning Mount and the Hairy Craig is a small but striking 'dry valley'. This arcuate hollow was trenched by marginal melt-waters when the ice sheet had shrunk northwards and left exposed the high ground of the Lammermuir area to the south. The channel turns at right angles to the general trend of the numerous dry valleys of the northern flanks of the Lammermuir Hills, which have an east-north-easterly direction parallel to the margin of the shrinking ice. It was presumably formed by water locally escaping northwards down a crevasse into the River Tyne hollow.

14. Traprain Law: Phonolite Laccolith

The rock of Traprain Law (14) is a very fresh phonolite, rather variable in colour, composed of orthoclase, green soda-augite, olivine (fayalite), analcite, nepheline and sodalite. The dome shape of the Law is original; platy joints, well seen in the quarry, are everywhere parallel to the upper surface, near which the rapidly cooled rock is fine-grained and flow-banded. Erosion has done little more than remove the covering of tilted sediments. During quarrying operations large xenoliths of baked shale (6 ft. across) and of sandstone (9 ft. and 29 ft. 6 in. in length), and small sedimentary and igneous xenoliths, have been found in the phonolite.

At various times collectors have obtained from the quarry good specimens of analcite, prehnite, pectolite, natrolite, apophyllite, datolite, anhydrite, selenite and stilpnomelane. Nepheline and sodalite cannot be recognized in the field. The presence of the latter mineral (which is in anhedral form) is notable, for no other occurrence is known in Britain. Euhedral sodalite, formerly believed to be present in a rock of the Assynt district of the north-west Highlands, has recently been shown by Professor C. E. Tilley (1958, p. 159) to be nosean.

REFERENCES

BENNETT, J. A. E., 1945. Some Occurrences of Leucite in East Lothian. *Trans. Edin. Geol. Soc.*, vol. 14, pt. i, pp. 41–43.

CLOUGH, C. T. *et al.*, 1910. The Geology of East Lothian, *Mem. Geol. Surv.*, Chapters 8, 9, 10.

DAY, T. C., 1930–32. *Trans. Edin. Geol. Soc.*, vol. 12, pp. 252–255 and 338–41 (sediment xenoliths in Traprain Law phonolite); 256–9 (dyke in Bangly Quarry); 234–5 (analyses of Traprain Law phonolite); 264–6 (analysis of Skid Hill trachyte or quartz-banakite).

HATCH, F. H., 1892. The Lower Carboniferous Volcanic Rocks of East Lothian (Garleton Hills). *Trans. Roy. Soc. Edin.*, vol. 37, pp. 115–26.

MACGREGOR, A. G., 1945. The Mineral Resources of the Lothians. *Geol. Surv. Wartime Pamph.*, No. 45, pp. 23–25, 30.

——and ENNOS, F. R., 1922. The Traprain Law Phonolite. *Geol. Mag.*, vol. 59, pp. 514–23.

TILLEY, C. E., 1958. Some new Chemical Data on Assemblages of the Assynt alkali suite. *Trans. Edin. Geol. Soc.*, vol. 17, pt. ii, pp. 156–64.

TOMKEIEFF, S. I., 1952. Analcite-Trachybasalt Inclusions in the Phonolite of Traprain Law. *Trans. Edin. Geol. Soc.*, vol. 15, pp. 360–73.

A. G. MacGregor

NORTH BERWICK

O.S. One-inch Map, Seventh Series, Sheets 56 and 63
G.S. One-inch Map, Sheet 41 (Scotland)
G.S. One-inch Map, Sheet 33 (Scotland)
Route-map p. 72

THE rocks which occur in the vicinity of North Berwick belong to the volcanic facies of the Scottish Lower Carboniferous. These beds, which have been more precisely assigned to the Calciferous Sandstone Measures, are poorly exposed in the inland area, but there are excellent exposures on the shores of the Firth of Forth both east and west of North Berwick.

The pyroclastic rocks in this volcanic assemblage are of particular interest, for besides bedded tuffs and agglomerates there are exposed, in the nine miles of coastline between Gullane and Peffer Sands, twelve large volcanic vents dissected by marine erosion. Five of these occur on the shore between Tantallon and North Berwick Pier; they pierce a series of bedded rocks and are themselves cut by a number of basic intrusions. The following account is concerned primarily with this section, which may be covered adequately in about six hours.

There is fairly easy access to the coast at many points along the described section and the recommended route may be negotiated without danger or difficulty except near high tide, when some parts become isolated and inaccessible. For this reason, and in order to obtain the maximum amount of foreshore-exposure, it is highly advisable that the traverse should commence not later than about three hours before low tide.

The rocks to be seen on this excursion include a thin series of white current-bedded sandstones and red marls, the Seacliff Group (Martin, 1955, Passage Group, *b–e*), which forms the upper part of the Passage Group bridging the gap between the Upper Old Red Sandstone and the Carboniferous. Above the sandstones comes the Oxroad Group (Martin, 1955, Volcanic Group, *f–h*), at least 450 ft. of green (or red near the top of the group) bedded tuffs and agglomerates, composed largely of basaltic material; near the top of this group tuffaceous sandstones, mudstones and thin cementstones are interbedded with the pyroclastic rocks. Rocks of both these groups are pierced by the coarse green basaltic agglomerate of the volcanic vents, some of which may have been the orifices from which were extruded the basic lavas (Martin, 1955, Volcanic Group, *i–k*) overlying the tuffs of the Oxroad Group at North Berwick Pier. Intrusion of the basaltic and basanitic sills and dykes may have been almost contemporaneous with the vulcanicity for they often form marginal sheets or isolated veinlets within the vents. Moreover, blocks of basaltic and basanitic composition commonly occur in the vent-agglomerates.

The general sequence of rocks in this coastal section, then, is as follows:

Basic Intrusions	
Basic Lavas	CALCIFEROUS
Volcanic Vents	SANDSTONE
Oxroad Group Tuffs	MEASURES
Seacliff Group Sandstones	

Because of the general westerly dip of the rocks an east-to-west traverse of the shore from Oxroad Bay to North Berwick

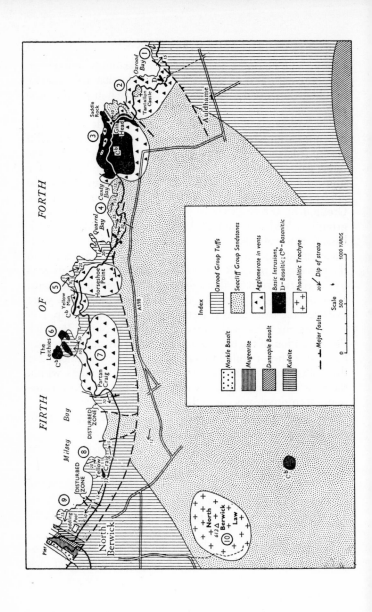

Index

Oxroad Group Tuffs		Markle Basalt	
Seacliff Group Sandstones		Mugearite	
Agglomerate in vents		Dunsapie Basalt	
Basic Intrusions, D=Basaltic; C^b=Basanitic		Kulaite	
Phonolitic Trachyte			

Major faults

Scale

0   500   1000 YARDS

20 Dip of strata

FIRTH   OF   FORTH

Oxroad Bay ①

② Tantallon Castle

Saddle Rock

③ Gin Head

C^b

④ Castleton Bay

Quarrel Bay

Horseshoe Point

⑤

C^b Yellow Man

The Leithies ⑥

C^b

⑦ Partan Craig

A198

Milsey Bay

⑧ Yellow Craig

DISTURBED ZONE

DISTURBED ZONE

⑨ Puddingstone Pool

Pier

North Berwick

⑩ North Berwick Law

613 △

C^b

Auldhame

is to be recommended, since the succession will thus be ascended in the course of the excursion.

A frequent bus and train service connects Edinburgh and North Berwick. From North Berwick the Dunbar bus should be taken, or the coast road to Dunbar (A.198) followed, as far as the sharp right turn at Auldhame Farm (595844). At this point, instead of following the main road to the right, it is necessary to take the farm road straight ahead for about 400 yd. to where a stone dividing-wall joins the road from the left. A rough path runs along the west side of this wall from a gate opening on to the road as far as the cliff-top and then down into Oxroad Bay (598845).

1. Oxroad Bay

The cliffs on the east side of this bay are formed in green, well-bedded tuffs of the Oxroad Group. Interbedded with the tuffs are a few thin, impersistent bands of tuffaceous sandstone and cementstone; the former contain small carbonized plant-fragments and very rare pelecypod-casts. The plant-fragments are most easily observed on the foreshore, where numerous ripple-marks of various types are exposed on the tops of the more sandy beds. Structures simulating small-scale uncon-formities occur in the bedded tuffs of the cliff and are probably of the nature of large 'wash-outs', formed as a result of the drying-out of the shallow, evanescent pools in which the vol-canic ashes, sands and calcareous muds appear to have been deposited. The unindurated sediment was soon eroded, the resultant hollows forming the site of later pools in which further deposition took place.

2. Tantallon Vent

A prominent fault runs north-north-eastwards through the east side of Oxroad Bay and beyond this, to the west, is the agglomerate of the Tantallon Vent. Near the fault this ag-glomerate is stratified with a steep easterly dip but on the west side of the bay, beyond a thick, bifurcating dyke of olivine-basalt, the vent-agglomerate is massive and unsorted with large blocks and bombs (mainly 'bread-crust' and 'spindle-shaped' types) of basaltic composition in a matrix of dark-green basaltic tuff.

Poorly stratified agglomerates of the type just described occupy most of the exposed part of the Tantallon Vent. Locally, however, the basaltic blocks become subordinate in amount to large pieces of pyroclastic and sedimentary rocks which, with few exceptions, are closely comparable with the rocks of the Seacliff and Oxroad Groups. Very large blocks of bedded tuff occur in jumbled profusion on the foreshore near the headland some 250 yd. north of the bifurcating dyke. This area may mark the site of a small explosive centre within the main vent.

At the top of the cliff, immediately below the foundations of the north-west walls of Tantallon Castle, there is a large mass of bedded sandstone, at least twenty feet long and twelve thick, and interpreted by T. C. Day as a fallen block incorporated in the agglomerate of the vent. However, the junction between sandstone and vent-rock appears to be strictly erosional while the stratification of the sediment is broadly parallel to that of the agglomerate, except near the sides of the mass where the sandstone appears to be banked against the agglomerate. These relations can best be explained as due to the deposition of the sandstone in a hollow eroded out of the ash within the temporarily quiescent volcano.

3. Gin Head Vent and Sill

The faulted west margin of the Tantallon Vent runs north-east through the bay just to the west of Tantallon Castle. Grey and white current-bedded sandstones, believed to be up-faulted representatives of the Seacliff Group, occur on the west side of the fault and are exposed near low-water mark as far as a prominent stack known as Saddle Rock. However, in the cliff on the west side of the bay mentioned above, there are exposed well-bedded tuffs and agglomerates marking the western boundary of the Gin Head Vent. The margin of this vent may be traced along the base of the cliff and can be seen to cut across a mass of unsorted red agglomerate which occupies a wide strip of foreshore about 150 yd. north-west of the margin of the Tantallon Vent. This red agglomerate lies in an older vent transected by the Gin Head Vent.

Forming the upper twenty feet of the cliff here, and as far as the Saddle Rock, is a sill of weathered analcite-basanite. Just east of the Saddle Rock the base of the intrusion descends to the shore and from this point westwards for about 600 yd. this sill occupies the cliffs and much of the foreshore. However, good vent-agglomerate appears in the cliff at Gin Head (594854), where it contains many ovoid bombs of basalt together with a very large block of current-bedded sandstone. Several large patches of coarse pyroclastic rock occur on the shore to the west of Gin Head and are interpreted as 'windows' in the base of the sill, revealing the underlying vent-agglomerate.

4. Canty and Quarrel Bays: Seacliff and Oxroad Groups

The sill terminates on the north-east side of Canty Bay (588854) and to the west of it there is a narrow strip of vent-agglomerate. Red marls with thin white sandstones abut sharply against this strip on its south-west side and dip at angles of 50°–60° towards it. This junction is taken to be the western margin of the Gin Head Vent.

The sandstones and red marls of the Seacliff Group are exposed on the foreshore in Canty Bay and in the south part of Quarrel Bay, where they are tightly folded and cut by several faults. The largest of these runs east-north-eastwards through the middle of the bay (582854) and brings down on its west side green stratified tuffs and agglomerates of the Oxroad Group. This fault may readily be traced on the shore at low tide by means of the beds of sandstone up-tilted against it.

5. Horseshoe and Yellow Man Vents

At Horseshoe Point (580855), some 300 yd. north-west of the above-mentioned fault, the bedded pyroclasts are cut off by a large mass of unstratified basaltic agglomerate forming part of the east end of the Horseshoe Vent. This agglomerate carries numerous large and small blocks of highly vesicular and amygdaloidal basalt which have proved useful in determining the extent of the vent. The vent-margin—essentially the discordant junction between coarse, unbedded vent-agglomerate and well-bedded tuff—is very well displayed on the shore and may be followed westwards for over 400 yd. until it is cut off by a basanitic dyke which forms a large stack on the shore, just below high-water-mark.

This intrusion is here coincident with the eastern boundary of yet another volcanic vent of relatively small extent, the Yellow Man Vent. From the configuration of this junction the Yellow Man Vent appears to be of later date than the contiguous Horseshoe Vent. The basanitic dyke swings abruptly to the west near high-water mark and, just east of the prominent stack which gives its name to the vent, it bifurcates to include a large mass of baked agglomerate. The dyke soon re-unites to form the eminence of the Yellow Man (575857), on the south side of which there is an unusually coarse development of the vent-agglomerate, with large blocks of bedded pyroclasts particularly abundant. A few yards to the south, on the foreshore and also in a small headland, narrow apophyses of the dyke may be observed to ramify through the agglomerate in a highly irregular manner, obscuring the western margin of the Yellow Man Vent which here runs west-north-west out to sea.

6. Leithies: Analcite-basanite

Occupying the shoreward exposures for the next 300 yd. is a shallow basin of thin stratified tuffs, sandstones and mudstones, with occasional grey and dark-blue cementstones.

These beds probably represent a fairly high horizon in the Oxroad Group. Injection into these rocks of the sheet of analcite-basanite which forms The Leithies (572858) has produced some interesting intrusive phenomena; these include the apparent injection of sedimentary material into the base of the sill, as may be seen on the south side of The Leithies.

7. Partan Craig Vent

Some 70 yd. south of the west end of The Leithies, across a stretch of sand, coarse poorly-bedded agglomerate is again encountered. This marks the north-east boundary of the large Partan Craig Vent, which is a roughly oval body extending on the shore from a point about 250 yd. south-west of the Yellow Man to the east end of Milsey Bay, and underlying much of the west end of the golf course. In the shore section the agglomerate within the vent is of very variable character. Along the north-east edge it is generally coarse with very large blocks of sedimentary and pyroclastic rocks in chaotic profusion. Elsewhere the agglomerate tends to be stratified and contains fewer large blocks.

Blocks of two distinctive rock-types are prominent among the ejectamenta in this vent. The first is a light grey or creamy cornstone, presumably derived from underlying Old Red Sandstone rocks. The other is a smoky-grey, medium-grained igneous rock with occasional pinkish patches. On microscopic examination this is revealed as a much altered nepheline-basanite.

8. Milsey Bay: Seacliff and Oxroad Groups

The western margin of the Partan Craig Vent may be traced along the foreshore near the base of the cliff which forms the eastern headland of Milsey Bay (568853). The rocks cut through by the vent are thin-bedded tuffs with many sandy and calcareous bands. Near the vent-margin these beds are nearly horizontal but a little farther to the west they dip at high angles and in several directions. This highly-disturbed zone is clearly defined and appears to be bounded on its east and west sides by low-angle faults. Recently it has been suggested that this area of disturbed beds has resulted from slumping of poorly consolidated sediments during the initial stages of vent formation in the adjacent Partan Craig Volcano (Martin, 1955, p. 98).

Yellow tuffaceous sandstones and red marls, presumably representatives of the Seacliff Group, occur in a faulted block on the west side of the highly-disturbed zone just described. However, the greater part of Milsey Bay is occupied by the bedded pyroclastic and sedimentary rocks of the Oxroad Group, with dominant north-south strike. These beds are green in colour at the east end of the bay but become increasingly more red to the west, beyond the basaltic plug of the Yellow Craig (561853).

About 200 yd. east of the paddling-pool, opposite Balfour Street, there is another zone of highly disturbed rocks—red stratified tuff with coarser, agglomeratic bands—which may represent a further region of slip.

9. Paddling pool: Leucite-kulaite and Basalt

Just to the west of the paddling-pool two flows of a peculiar purplish-brown lava are encountered, extending to the base of the Pier. Each flow is about 30 ft. thick and is highly scoriaceous near the top. The rock is very much altered and contains numerous phenocrysts of brown hornblende. Microscopically it has strong affinities with the mugearites but the presence of the hornblende (now mainly resorbed) and of analcite, which is believed to be replacing leucite, induced J. A. E. Bennett (1942, p. 35) to classify the rock as a *leucite-kulaite*.

Above the kulaite and forming the eastern face of the Pier (554857) is about 40 ft. of Dunsapie basalt carrying conspicuous phenocrysts of plagioclase, titanaugite and olivine, and somewhat vesicular near the base. Following immediately upon the basalt are two flows, each 15 ft. thick, of a red-weathering, non-porphyritic mugearite. The top of the upper flow is extremely vesicular, with elongate cavities up to 2 in. long. Finally, a fifty-foot flow of Markle basalt, with prominent lath-like phenocrysts of plagioclase, lies disconformably on top of the mugearite.

10. North Berwick Law: Phonolitic Trachyte

Should time permit, there are two inland exposures which merit examination. The more accessible of these is North Berwick Law, a plug-like intrusion of phonolitic trachyte. This may be reached from the Pier by proceeding via Quality Street and the High Street to the Law Road, then straight up the hill, following the B.1347 road for about 800 yd. to where the road turns sharply to the right. From this corner a footpath leads to the large quarry on the south side of the Law (554840).

The red-mottled trachyte which occurs in the quarry is somewhat weathered but the non-porphyritic, medium-grained and highly feldspathic nature of the rock can still be readily detected. Several large curved joint-planes are conspicuous on the north wall of the quarry, dipping at moderately low angles to the south. Fresh specimens of the trachyte are best obtained from the crags halfway up the west face of the Law. Here, the platy character of the rock is well displayed —a feature induced by marked flow-alignment of the feldspars.

11. Kingston Schoolhouse: Striae on Mugearite

The lava sequence of North Berwick Pier is repeated in the crags of Kingston Hill, which lies about a mile and a quarter south-west of the Law and may be reached by continuing along road B.1347. On the rounded hummocks of mugearitic lava at the roadside opposite Kingston schoolhouse (543824) there are numerous glacial striae. These run parallel to a number of remarkable, deeply-incised grooves or channels, up to

14 in. deep and 15 ft. long, shallower to the west and asymmetrical in cross-section. Striae and grooves trend east-southeast and presumably both have resulted from glacial action.

REFERENCES

DAY, T. C., 1925–1930. Several papers in *Trans. Edin. Geol. Soc.*, vols. 11–12.

MACGREGOR, M. and MACGREGOR, A. G., 1948. Midland Valley of Scotland, 2nd edit. rev., *Brit. Reg. Geol., Geol. Surv.*, pp. 34–69.

MARTIN, N. R., 1955. Lower Carboniferous Volcanism near North Berwick, Scotland. *Bull. Geol. Surv.*, No. 7, pp. 90–99.

BENNETT, J. A. E., 1942. Some Occurrences of Leucite in East Lothian. *Trans. Edin. Geol. Soc.*, vol. 14, pp. 34–52.

GILBERT KELLING

Tantallon Castle standing on cliffs of vent agglomerate

DUNBAR

O.S. One-inch Map, Seventh Series, Sheet 63
G.S. One-inch Map, Sheet 33 (Scotland)
Route-map p. 82

＊

DUNBAR lying twenty-five miles east of Edinburgh, with main-line and A.1 road connexions, is well known to non-geologists for its beauty, historical associations, dry climate, red-soil potatoes, and golf. To geologists it offers, in its immediate neighbourhood, exceptionally interesting exposures of Calciferous Sandstone volcanic necks; while at no great distance lie: Hutton's farm (Sligh Houses north-east of Duns); his classic unconformity at Siccar Point; more Calciferous Sandstone igneous rocks at Traprain Law and North Berwick; a four-mile coastal stretch of Carboniferous Limestone between Broxburn and Skateraw; and glacial-drainage phenomena margining the Lammermuirs. For the half-day excursion outlined below, the party should travel by road to the shore north of Belhaven and then on foot make for the north-west peninsula shown on the route-map. Alternatively a fast train may be taken to Dunbar, whence Belhaven can be reached on foot or by bus. The subsequent walk is one and a half miles along the coast, mostly by a cliff-top path or parade. Low tide is essential.

The following account is merely a summary of what H. B. Maufe supplied in the East Lothian *Memoir of the Geological Survey*, 1910, where additional information is available. The writer still vividly recalls the pleasure and instruction he

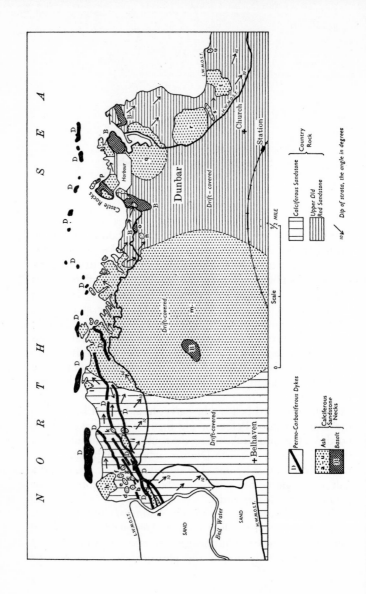

N O R T H   S E A

Castle Rocks

Harbour

Dunbar

Church

Station

+ Belhaven

Bail Water

SAND

SAND

L.W.M.O.S.T.

H.W.M.O.S.T.

L.W.M.O.S.T.

Drift-covered

Drift-covered

Drift-covered

Scale

0   ½ MILE

D   Permo-Carboniferous Dykes

Ash
Basalt   Calciferous
              Sandstone Necks

Calciferous Sandstone
Upper Old
Red Sandstone   Country
                            Rock

10   Dip of strata, the angle in degrees

received one day in 1904, when Maufe demonstrated to him his discoveries along this shore. Some of the nicer points are set among slippery rocks and seaweed, which renders them unsuitable for close examination by a party of mixed ages. Seniors who stick mainly to the path will, with a little faith, realize quite clearly the gist of the story, and juniors will be able to hammer a sufficient number of representative exposures.

The oldest rocks at Dunbar are a set of false-bedded sandstones, often red, sometimes purple, yellowish, or speckled. Wind-rounding of quartz grains has been noted in what seem to be the older members. The grains affected have often received a faceted outgrowth of secondary quartz after becoming coated with iron oxide. Small irregular concretions of cornstone, stained bright red by iron oxide, are common among the younger members. The staining is of later date than Old Red Sandstone times (Goodchild has suggested New Red Sandstone), since it equally affects succeeding Calciferous Sandstone cementstones. No fossils have been found in the Dunbar sandstones, but at one locality these pass under fossiliferous Calciferous Sandstone, and they agree lithologically with unquestionable Upper Old Red sandstones elsewhere in East Lothian. Maufe has mapped many faults on the Dunbar shore, often obviously of little throw. They have been omitted from the route-map to avoid confusion with other detail. Faulting, however, has controlled outcrops to a considerable extent. Thus Upper Old Red Sandstone supplies practically all the sedimentary outcrops seen east of the great ash neck lettered m; while Calciferous Sandstone furnishes all of them to the west of this neck, in spite of the dip in both formations being commonly directed east or south-east.

The Calciferous Sandstone sediments of Dunbar all belong to the Cementstone Group, the lowest subdivision of the Scottish Carboniferous, and they have yielded a few characteristic fossils. Some 300 ft. are exposed in a thin-bedded, rhythmic succession, repeating sandstone, shale, cementstone, shale, sandstone. A sandstone, about 50 ft. thick, yellowish, false-bedded and micaceous, occurs towards the middle. There is widespread staining with red oxide of iron. This is particularly the case with the cementstones, which only preserve their original greenish or bluish-green colour in their lowest (most westerly) exposures. Maufe quotes two comparative analyses of reddened and unreddened examples; but the subject deserves fuller inquiry. He also found a cementstone bed in which reddening affected only the top inch with irregular extensions down along joints.

There are about a score of ash necks seen at Dunbar, all undoubtedly of Calciferous Sandstone age. They range in diameter from a few yards to over half a mile. They are separately lettered *a–u* in the map (p. 82), and are mostly filled with a 'sandy tuff, containing decomposing glass lapilli, blocks of amygdaloidal basalt and of the various types of sediment belonging to the Old Red and Calciferous Sandstone series. This agglomerate is sometimes pierced by a plug of basic igneous rock. In one case only, that of the Dove Rock [o] situated 150 yd. west of Dunbar Castle, is the vent wholly filled by basalt, whilst a few of the small necks are filled merely with brecciated non-volcanic materials.' The basalt of the necks, whether occurring as fragments or as intrusions, is generally analcite-basalt. This agrees in character with a lava exposed in association with Calciferous Sandstone sediments in a faulted coastal outcrop less than a mile east of Dunbar, and also with a number of intrusions seen along the North Berwick shore.

A small group of approximately east-west quartz-dolerite dykes (D) is well exposed at low tide west of Dunbar. These dykes are petrologically very distinct from the intrusions of the Calciferous Sandstone necks and are much later, belonging to the Permo-Carboniferous. They aim across country at a couple of similar dykes at Port Seton and Prestonpans; and there are a few intermediate exposures in the Garleton Hills.

Cliffs at Dunbar often drop abruptly to the modern fore-shore, but sometimes there is an intervening platform belonging to the 25-ft. raised beach. The foreshore of to-day provides a striking miniature example of a plain of marine denudation.

1. Quartz-dolerite Dyke, Necks a–l

Having dismounted at Belhaven, the party will proceed north along the shore and will traverse most of the exposed portion of the Cementstone Group—though on this eastern shore the median sandstone is reduced (and seawards cut out) by faulting. A very curious feature of the foreshore here is the sharp division that the Biel Water, in its lowest reaches, follows between white sands of Belhaven Bay to the west and naked rock to the east, the latter extending up to high-water mark.

One of the quartz-dolerite dykes margins the north-west termination of the peninsula. It runs east-north-east rather than east, and has a marked tendency to split into narrow branches some of which, but not all, follow manifest minor faults. One of the most interesting phenomena of the district is the manner in which this group of dykes has cut or touched several pre-existing necks. In two cases (*c* and *k* of route-map) Maufe found that thin dykes of the group are interrupted by small necks but 'in each case the dyke is chilled against the neck and also sends small tongues of dolerite into it. In all other instances [*a, i, j*], the dykes clearly cut the vents, and in their neighbourhood have often undergone alteration to "white trap".' It seems that early east-north-east fractures first determined the location of the necks concerned and then, after long ages, that of the subsequent dykes. The necks are filled with breccia of the local sediments, including composite angular blocks up to five yards in length. External strata close to the neck margins are sharply broken or bent down, indicating drag due to subsidence of the contents. This is an extremely common feature of neck junctions everywhere in the world.

Another point of special interest may be quoted from Maufe's account: 'Some of these necks pierce the summit of low anticlines or domes which are overlapped by the succeeding beds, thus proving that the folds in these cases are contemporaneous with the deposition of the sediments. In one example, the overlapping beds seem to cover over one end of the neck, so that these small vents are perhaps contemporaneous with the surrounding beds of the Cementstone series.' Maufe does not specify the necks concerned, probably *d–f*.

Obviously the foreshore west of the big neck *m* affords plenty of material for the younger participants, without visiting neck *h* filled with 'reddish or yellowish tuff', or neck *l* choked with breccia. The main quartz-dolerite dyke lies just out to sea, but is quite conspicuous. Probably some seniors will be satisfied after actual examination of neck *a* cut by two narrow dykes.

2. Neck m

Two hundred and fifty yards east of the end of the peninsula, high-water mark is walled, and those not prepared to scramble should leave the foreshore here and walk to the start of the narrow parade where it scales with steps a prominent red cliff. Here is the edge of the great neck *m*, clearly seen on the foreshore transgressing the sediments of the Cementstone Group which show the customary down-drag at contact. Those on the foreshore will find, 15 to 50 yd. inside the neck, a conspicuous sandstone dyke, varying from a few inches to several feet in width and traceable for 200 yd. Having examined it they should climb to rejoin their comrades on the parade.

Neck *m* is filled with red, sandy stratified tuff with angular fragments of basalt, sandstone, etc. It is a rewarding experience to walk on the parade at the cliff edge across this great, wonderfully exposed neck.

3. Sediments

The eastern boundary of neck *m*, not far beyond a war memorial, is irregular, but the accustomed external down-drag is again in evidence. On this side Upper Old Red Sandstone is the country-rock. On reaching it the party should leave the parade and proceed south-east at high-water mark to where the cliff begins to jut out again. Here, in the corner, presumed Upper Old Red Sandstone is covered by indubitable Carboniferous: cornstone-bearing sandstones (the cornstone concretions are reddened) pass under sediments which in their lower part (on the foreshore) contain two thin bands of impure, reddened cementstone, and higher up (at the foot of the cliff) have yielded Carboniferous fossils. Some shale in the cliff above the fossil band is of characteristic greenish tint. The Carboniferous rocks are cut off to the north-east by a north-west fault accompanied by some very complex structures.

4. Necks o–u

On regaining the parade the party soon obtains a good view of the Dove Rock, *o*, alongside an artificial bathing pool. It is a plug of analcite-basalt, around which down-drag is as pronounced as it is around the ash necks. The Castle Rocks, seen beyond, are formed of an irregular dyke-like intrusion of analcite-basalt, mainly penetrating sandstone but also traversing an ash neck, *p*, in which the ash is partly red, partly green. To the east the Victoria Harbour lies mostly on Old Red Sandstone which separates the Castle neck from another, *q*, the outcrop of which embraces the whole of the Old Harbour built for Cromwell. Ash in *q* is pierced by a low-angled, columnar sheet of felspathic, slightly porphyritic basalt, well exposed between the two harbours. The eastern margin of *q*, with ash against sandstone and with characteristic external down-drag, can easily be traced on the foreshore east of the Old Harbour.

A few more necks, *r–u*, lie to the south-east; but it is assumed that the party will want to stop here and explore the two harbours and what remains of the Castle. The latter is a complete ruin. In its day it sheltered Edward II after Bannockburn and Queen Mary after Kirk o' Field; but by the time Cromwell awaited the Lord's deliverance of his enemy Leslie into his hand, the old stronghold had faded out of history. Probably much of its material has been converted to peaceful uses in the walls of the two harbours.

REFERENCES

CLOUGH, C. T., *et al.*, 1910. The Geology of East Lothian. *Mem. Geol. Surv.*

E. B. BAILEY

GRANTSHOUSE, SICCAR POINT, COVE, CATCRAIG

O.S. One-inch Map, Seventh Series, Sheet 63
G.S. One-inch Map, Sheets 33 and 34 (Scotland)
Route-maps pp. 90, 96, 98

THE Siccar Point excursion consists of four separate localities or sections, any three of which make a reasonable day's trip. They are:

	Time	Walking distance
(1) The Grantshouse anticline in Silurian greywackes - -	about 1 hour	—
(2) The Siccar Point unconformity - - - - -	1–2 hours	$\frac{1}{2}$ mile
(3) The Pease Bay—Cove Coastal section of Upper Old Red Sandstone and Lower Carboniferous rocks - - -	2–3 hours	1 mile
(4) The Catcraig shore section of Carboniferous Lower Limestone Group rocks - -	1–2 hours	$1\frac{1}{2}$ miles

At high tide the wave-cut platform of the Pease Bay - Cove coast section is impassable and the limestones of the Catcraig shore are mostly covered. The former should not be attempted within *two* hours of high tide on an ebb tide, and *five* hours on a flood tide; the latter is best seen within three hours of low tide. The Siccar Point unconformity, although better exposed

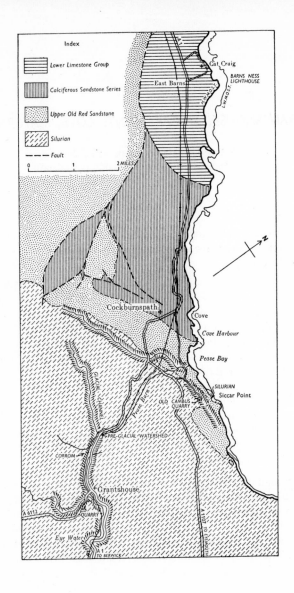

at low tide, is still spectacular at high tide. Since the four localities occur within 10 miles of each other they can be taken in the order best suited to the state of the tide.

1. Grantshouse: Folded Llandovery Sediments

Turn south off the A.1 road in Grantshouse village on to A.6112, cross the railway bridge, and the quarry is on the left-hand side of the road some 400 yd. from the main A.1 road. Two sections are shown. In the main quarry a cross-section of an anticline in greywackes and shales of Llandovery age is exposed: the quarry flank facing the railway is an instructive dip face of greywacke showing good joint patterns.

The anticline has an almost horizontal axis trending south-west with an axial plane dipping steeply to the south-east. The core of the fold is cut by a minor reversed fault trending parallel to the fold-axis and down-throwing the strata 5 ft. to the south-east. Simple tectonic structures are well displayed. Cleavage is developed in the shales towards the top of greywacke beds and trends parallel to the fold axis, but is fanned out, suggesting development during folding. Slickensiding has resulted from differential movement between the greywacke beds during folding and is parallel to the a-axis of the fold. The joint system consists of cross joints symmetrically distributed with respect to b, and ac joints of which the quarry face is a good composite example. The joint system is well shown on the northern flank of the fold facing the railway.

The rocks are dominantly greywackes with thin shale bands. The greywackes show graded bedding and sedimentary structures such as groove and flute casts. On some surfaces these structures have been intensified by load casting and the resulting small flame structures can be seen in cross-sections. The rocks are unfossiliferous. In composition, the greywackes resemble the rocks of Hazelbank (p. 123) in that they contain augite and hornblende in addition to quartz, feldspar and various rock fragments.

2. Siccar Point: Hutton's Classic Unconformity

Siccar Point lies on the coast due north of Grantshouse. West of the A.1 road 1¾ miles to the north of Grantshouse the railway line is cut through a corrom which can be identified by the disappearing line of telegraph poles along the railway. The corrom forms a minor watershed in the valley (Kendall and Bailey, 1908, pp. 26–27). Continuing on road A.1, some 3 miles to the north, turn right on to road A.1107. This road crosses the post-glacial gorge of the Pease Burn almost at once and the quarry road to Siccar Point turns off 500 yd. on the left after the narrow bridge over the gorge. Keep to the right fork of this road, cross the small iron-grid bridge (with care it takes a bus 8 ft. wide!) and continue along an extremely fine marginal drainage channel (Kendall and Bailey, 1908, general map) into Old Cambus quarry where there is ample room for any vehicle to turn. Continue by foot through the north-east gate in the quarry and strike obliquely left up the hillside towards the far corner of the field, 200 ft. below which lies Siccar Point and Hutton's unconformity. From the cliffs a fine panorama can be seen to the north-west of the Upper Old Red Sandstone grading up into the grey sandstones of the Lower Carboniferous (Pease Bay - Cove section). The light-house in the middle distance is Barns Ness (Lower Limestone Group) and in the far distance the Bass Rock juts out from the sea with North Berwick Law lying inland slightly to the west. Both are plugs of phonolitic trachyte.

Siccar Point speaks eloquently for itself and needs little description. An inclined uneven basement of vertical grey-wackes and shales of Llandovery age is covered unconform-ably by gently dipping dull-red breccia and sandstone of Upper Old Red Sandstone age. The breccia is composed of greywacke fragments.

Historically the Siccar Point unconformity is world-famous because of its discoverer, James Hutton, the first geologist to grasp the true significance of such a structure. John Playfair's

(1805, pp. 71–72) description of the joint discovery deserves to be read on the spot.

'The ridge of the Lammer-muir Hills in the south of Scotland, consists of primary micaceous schistus, and extends from St Abb's-head westward, till it joins the metalliferous mountains about the sources of the Clyde. The sea-coast affords a transverse section of this alpine tract at its eastern extremity, and exhibits the change from the primary to the secondary strata, both on the south and on the north. Dr HUTTON wished particularly to examine the latter of these, and on this occasion Sir JAMES HALL and I had the pleasure to accompany him. We sailed in a boat from Dunglass, on a day when the fineness of the weather permitted us to keep close to the foot of the rocks which line the shore in that quarter, directing our course southwards, in search of the termination of the secondary strata. We made for a high rocky point or head-land, the SICCAR, near which, from our observations on shore, we knew that the object we were in search of was likely to be discovered. On landing at this point, we found that we actually trode on the primeval rock, which forms alternately the base and the summit of the present land. It is here a micaceous schistus, in beds nearly vertical, highly indurated, and stretching from south-east to north-west. The surface of this rock runs with a moderate ascent from the level of low-water, at which we landed, nearly to that of high-water, where the schistus has a thin covering of red horizontal sandstone laid over it; and this sandstone, at the distance of a few yards farther back, rises into a very high perpendicular cliff. Here, therefore, the immediate contact of the two rocks is not only visible, but is curiously dissected and laid open by the action of the waves. The rugged tops of the schistus are seen penetrating into the horizontal beds of sandstone, and the lowest of these last form a breccia containing fragments of schistus, some round and others angular, united by an arenaceous cement.

'Dr. HUTTON was highly pleased with appearances that set in so clear a light the different formations of the parts which compose the exterior crust of the earth, and where all the circumstances were combined that could render the observation satisfactory and precise. On us who saw these phenomena for the first time, the impression made will not easily be forgotten. The palpable evidence presented to us, of one of the most extraordinary and important facts in the natural history of the earth, gave a reality and substance to those theoretical speculations, which, however probable, had never till now been directly authenticated by the testimony of the senses. We often said to ourselves, What clearer evidence could we have had of the different formation of these rocks, and of the long interval which separated their formation, had we actually seen them emerging from the bosom of the deep? We felt ourselves necessarily carried back to the time when the schistus on which we stood was yet at the bottom of the sea, and when the sandstone before us was only beginning to be deposited, in the shape of sand or mud, from the waters of a superincumbent ocean. An epocha still more remote presented itself, when even the most ancient of these rocks instead of standing upright in vertical beds, lay in horizontal planes at the bottom of the sea, and was not yet disturbed by that immeasurable force which has burst asunder the solid pavement of the globe. Revolutions still more remote appeared in the distance of this extraordinary perspective. The mind seemed to grow giddy by looking so far into the abyss of time; and while we listened with earnestness and admiration to the philosopher who was now unfolding to us the order and series of these wonderful events, we became sensible how much farther reason may sometimes go than imagination can venture to follow. As for the rest, we were truly fortunate in the course we had pursued in this excursion; a great number of other curious and important facts presented themselves, and we returned, having collected, in one day, more ample materials for future speculation, than have sometimes resulted from years of diligent and laborious research.'

It is perhaps better to examine the Old Cambus quarry after Siccar Point has been visited. The greywackes in the quarry dip to the south-east and are the right way up. New quarry faces frequently show excellent ripple-marks and other upper-surface features. Flute casts are to be found in small outcrops on the grassy slopes behind the north-west quarry face. Grapto-lites may be collected from the grey, greenish and red shales behind the weighbridge and include *Monograptus galaensis*, *M. pandus*, *M. marri* and *M. spiralis*, indicating Llandovery age.

3. Pease Bay - Cove: Upper Old Red Sandstone and Lower Car-boniferous (map p. 96)

Picturesque Pease Bay rimmed by cliffs of gently dipping Upper Old Red Sandstone is reached by returning along the road from Old Cambus Quarry and, after taking the right turn, walking down the steep hill to the shore immediately before the short rise onto the Eyemouth road. If a bus is being used it should be sent on to await the party at the junction with the main road a quarter of a mile east of Cove.

The section begins at the north-west end of Pease Bay with false-bedded red sandstone which contains well-rounded grains. Rare scales of *Holoptychius nobilissimus* indicate an Upper Old Red Sandstone age for these rocks. The red sand-stones grade upwards into a grey sandstone on which a thin bed of cementstone breccia, taken to be the base of the Car-boniferous in this area, lies disconformably. The Carboni-ferous succession here is probably not older than Visean and is as follows, (Clough *et al.* 1910, p. 44):

								ft.
Oil Shales	-	-	-	-	-	-	-	1
Greenish-grey and purple marls		-	-	-	-	20
Cove Harbour Sandstone	-	-	-	-	-	85

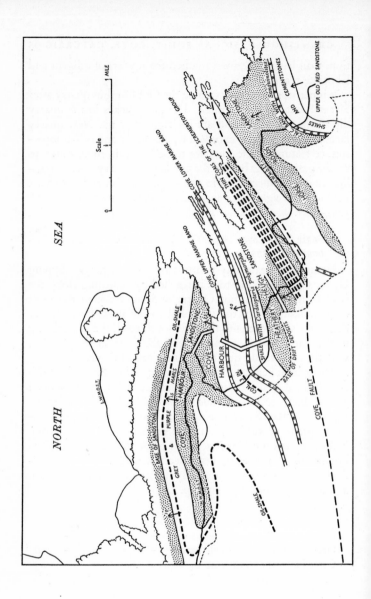

NORTH SEA

Scale

0 ½ 1 MILE

L.W.M.O.S.T.

BASE OF SANDSTONE

PURPLE & MARL Ls.

GREY COVE HARBOUR SANDSTONE

L.W.M.O.S.T.

OIL-SHALE

COVE HARBOUR

COVE HARBOUR

COVE UPPER MARINE BAND

COVE LOWER MARINE BAND

COVE OF THE SCREMERSTON GROUP

SHALE WITH Cardiopteris polymorpha

HEATHERY HEUGH SANDSTONE

THIN COALS OF THE SCREMERSTON GROUP

BASE OF DRIFT DEPOSITS

OIL-SHALE

COVE FAULT

SANDSTONE

COAL-BED WITH Stangaria

UPPER OLD RED SANDSTONE

SHALES AND CEMENTSTONES

Sandstone and shale - - - - - -	27
Cove Upper Limestone - - - - -	$1\frac{1}{2}$
Sandstone, shale, fireclay and coal - - - -	64
Cove Lower Limestone - - - - -	15
Heathery Heugh Sandstone - - - - -	92
Yellow and red sandstone with purple-red marls and grey marls - - - - - - -	67
Scremerston coals - - - - - -	85
Kip Carle Sandstone - - - - - -	50
Fault	
Cementstone conglomerates, sandstone, shale, greenish and purplish cementstones - - - -	300
Horse Roads Sandstone - - - - -	143
Calcareous band with *Sanguinolites* - - - -	$1\frac{1}{2}$
Cementstone and shale with cementstone conglomerate (Eastern Hole Conglomerate) - -	57
Upper Old Red Sandstone	

Ostracods, plant fragments and lamellibranchs including *Sanguinolites* may be collected from the cementstone beds. The Horse Roads Sandstone is false-bedded and shows slump structures and concretions. The Kip Carle Sandstone forms the prominent point beyond the cliffs of the Horse Roads Sandstone, and the Cove Fault is adjudged to run in the small bay between the two sandstones. Thin coals, sandstones and shales follow the steeply dipping Kip Carle Sandstone and are correlated with the Scremerston Coal Group of Northumberland.

The Cove Marine Bands can be accurately located with respect to the Cove Harbour sea wall. The lower and more easily found band—a calcareous sandstone 15 ft. thick—crops out 30 ft. south of the angle in the harbour wall. Fossils are abundant but mostly fragmentary and include *Productus redesdalensis*, *Composita*, *Punctospirifer scabricosta*, Sanguinolitids and Nuculids. The upper marine band crops out at the seaward

H

Siccar Point. Gently dipping Old Red Sandstone lying unconformably on vertical Silurian greywackes and shales

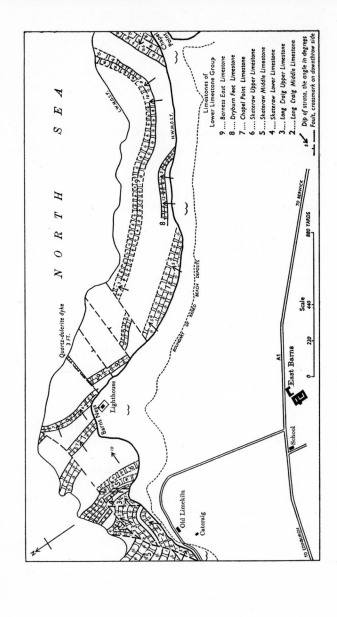

N O R T H   S E A

Quartz-dolerite dyke 3 FT.

Lighthouse

Barns Ness

L.W.M.O.S.T.

H.W.M.O.S.T.

BOUNDARY OF RAISED BEACH DEPOSITS

Chapel Point

Old Limekiln

Catcraig

School

East Barns

A1

TO EDINBURGH

TO BERWICK

Limestones of
Lower Limestone Group

9 .... Barness East Limestone
8 .... Dryburn Feet Limestone
7 .... Chapel Point Limestone
6 .... Skateraw Upper Limestone
5 .... Skateraw Middle Limestone
4 .... Skateraw Lower Limestone
3 .... Long Craig Upper Limestone
2 .... Long Craig Middle Limestone

Dip of strata, the angle in degrees
Fault, crossmark on downthrow side

Scale
0   220   440   880 YARDS

end of the harbour wall and consists of some 3 ft. of calcareous shales and impure limestone yielding *Punctospirifer scabricosta*, *Aviculopecten*, and Orthoceratids. These bands are the oldest fully marine horizons in the Scottish Carboniferous. Wilson (1952) has collected from nearby inland exposures of the lower marine band excellent specimens of the goniatite *Beyrichoceratoides redesdalensis* indicating the presence of the Cracoean (B) stage. He also gives a full list of fossils obtained from these bands.

The path to Cove village and the main road leads from the harbour through a tunnel cut in the Cove Harbour Sandstone.

4. Catcraig: Lower Limestone Group: (map p. 98)

Five miles to the north-west of Cove turn off road A.1 at the junction (716764) near East Barns on to the narrow road leading to the Barns Ness Lighthouse. (It is difficult to turn a bus at the end of this road.

It is best to leave private cars just through the gate and take the track towards the north and west. This leads past the old limekilns to a second gate where the Catcraig section begins. This point marks the eastern end of the beach, White Sands. The section to the east can then be treated either as a detailed stratigraphical succession of the Lower Limestone Group or more simply as a good collecting ground for corals, brachiopods and other fossils.

The succession, in which the numbers relate to the limestones numbered on the map, is as follows (Clough *et al.* 1910, p. 135):

							ft.
	Massive, current-bedded sandstone						
9.	Barness East Limestone –	–	–	–	–		2–6
	Strata, mainly sandstones	–	–	–	–		50
8.	Dryburn Foot Limestone	–	–	(approx.)			2
	Sandstone and shale	–	–	–	–	–	10

7. Chapel Point Limestone – – (approx.)				10
Sandstone, fireclay and shale with coal smut –				103
6. Skateraw Upper Limestone –	–	–	–	1–2
Black shale – – – –	–	–	–	3–5
5. Skateraw Middle Limestone –	–	–	–	16–18
Coal (6 in.), shale, fireclay etc.	–	–	–	8½
4. Skateraw Lower Limestone –	–	–	–	2–4
Sandstone and shale –	–	–	–	23
3. Long Craig Upper Limestone	–	–	–	18
Shale with patchy thin coal –	–	–	–	5
2. Long Craig Middle Limestone	–	–	–	3–6
Sandstone and shale –	–	–	–	25
1. Long Craig Lower Limestone and shales –		–	–	39

The lowermost limestone (Long Craig Lower) is not seen in this section which begins in the easily recognized Long Craig Middle Limestone. This bed is characterized by an abundance of *Lithostrotion junceum* and *L. pauciradiale* (spaghetti- and macaroni-rock) and below the corals the limestone is white in colour and nodular. The most striking feature (well seen on the shore below the old limekilns), is the presence of large potholes in the top of the limestone. The potholes appear to be of Carboniferous age since they are filled in part by the overlying fireclay. Above the overlying thin coal there is an extremely fossiliferous shale yielding numerous specimens of Productids and lamellibranchs. This shale forms part of the small ledge about 4 ft. high, at high-tide mark.

The Long Craig Upper Limestone yields in abundance large solitary corals such as *Koninckophyllum echinatum*, *Aulophyllum fungites*, *Dibunophyllum* and Zaphrentids as well as *Lithostrotion*. *Gigantoproductus* occurs in the Skateraw Lower Limestone, *Saccaminopsis fusulinaformis* can be obtained from the Skateraw Middle Limestone, and *Taonurus cauda-galli*, the trace fossil possibly representing the feeding movements of some unknown invertebrate, can be collected from several beds near the lighthouse in the vicinity of the Chapel Point Limestone. About 100 yd. to the east, the Barness East Limestone is a dark grey, finely jointed cream- or buff-weathering band which lies below a thick succession of massive and current-bedded sandstones. For completeness, the Dryburn Foot Limestone may be examined in exposures some three-quarters of a mile east of the lighthouse.

REFERENCES

CLOUGH, C. T., *et al.*, 1910. The Geology of East Lothian. *Mem. Geol. Surv.*

KENDALL, P. F. and BAILEY, E. B., 1908. The Glaciation of East Lothian south of the Garleton Hills. *Trans. Roy. Soc. Edin.*, vol. 16, pp. 1–31.

PLAYFAIR, J., 1805. Biographical Account of the late Dr James Hutton. *Trans. Roy. Soc. Edin.*, vol. 5, part III, pp. 39–99.

PRINGLE, J., 1948. The South of Scotland. 2nd edit. *British Regional Geology, Geol. Surv.*

WILSON, H., 1952. The Cove marine bands in East Lothian and their relation to the ironstone shale and limestone of Redesdale, Northumberland. *Geol. Mag.*, vol. 89, pp. 305–319.

G. Y. CRAIG

EILDON HILLS

O.S. One-inch Map, Sheet 70
G.S. One-inch Map, Sheet 25 (Scotland)
Route-map and Section, p. 106

—

FOR a party proceeding from Edinburgh on this excursion the best transport arrangement is travel by a specially engaged bus and for the purposes of this account the journey is described as if being made in this manner. A full day is required to complete the itinerary, but if a shorter day is desired one of the following abridged programmes is suggested:

(1) Chiefswood and Bowdenmoor quarries—Little Hill.
(2) Bowdenmoor Quarry—Little Hill—columnar felsite of Wester Hill—summit of Mid Hill.
(3) Little Hill—summit of Mid Hill—North Hill.
    Parties are warned that there are rifle ranges on the low ground west of Mid Hill and these are sometimes in use on Saturdays.

Introduction

Topographically, the Eildon Hills form a pleasing profile bordering the south side of the Tweed valley in the romantic district of Melrose in Roxburghshire. The hills consist of three principal summits rising above the cultivated lands and groves of the countryside. Eildon Mid Hill reaches a height of 1385 ft. above sea-level while the North and Wester hills attain heights of 1327 and 1216 ft. respectively. A smaller hill, known as Little Hill, lies on the west side of the valley between the Mid and Wester hills. Geologically, the Eildons have been regarded as the remnant of a large composite laccolite consisting of several sheets of intermediate and acid rocks intruded into sedimentary strata of the Upper Old Red Sandstone and thus of later date. Little Hill is a small volcanic vent of agglomerate, with an intruded plug consisting of two types of basalt, and almost certainly of later date than the acid rocks of the Eildons. A quarry in the great volcanic pipe at Chiefswood, on the south-west of Melrose, and another quarry at Bowdenmoor usually have been regarded by the authors as part of their excursion to the Eildon Hills and are dealt with in this itinerary. A comprehensive account of the igneous rocks of the Melrose district was published by Lady Rachel Workman McRobert in 1914 and quotations in the text are from her paper.

The outward route is by Soutra and Lauderdale. On departing from the city the bus proceeds by Dalkeith Road, crossing the Pentland Fault just west of Craigmillar; thence traversing the Midlothian coal-basin by Dalkeith and over the Lower Carboniferous rocks of Pathhead to cross the Southern Upland Fault a short distance south of the village of Fala. Here the road ascends to the higher Lammermoor tableland of Ordovician rocks, with relic-areas of Upper Old Red Sandstone conglomerates around Soutra Hill. On this upland plateau lies the local watershed between the Tyne and Tweed drainage systems. After crossing the watershed the route reaches the deeply-cut gullies of the head streams of the Leader Water with outcrops of Ordovician greywackes, grits and shales. As the way advances into Lauderdale red-stained conglomerates of the Upper Old Red Sandstone underlie the superficial deposits in this pre-Old Red Valley and are connected to the main mass of Upper Old Red Sandstone of the Merse of Berwickshire. The soil is everywhere of a rich red colour. Following the Leader Water the road descends for some 12 miles over these Old Red rocks and passes on to Silurian greywackes and shales near Earlston. In the vicinity of Earlston there are several igneous intrusions. One of these caps the Black Hill which forms a prominent feature of the landscape about a mile south of the village on the east side of the valley. The hill is composed of a sheet of trachyte intruded into sandstones of Upper Old Red Sandstone age. In an old quarry on the south side of the hill scales of *Holoptychius nobilissimus* have been found in the sandstones below the intrusion. McRobert (1914, p. 306) defines the intrusive rock as a 'porphyritic quartz-riebeckite-trachyte' which can be matched in the Eildon suite. At Leaderfoot the road enters the valley of the Tweed. At the south end of the bridge spanning the river the way turns sharp to the right and winds westwards past the site of the great Roman station called 'Trimontium' or the Camp by the Three Hills; its site, marked by a fine stone, lies close to the village of Newstead. From this hamlet the road runs over an alluvial flat of the Tweed and the historic town of Melrose, with its famous abbey, appears in view. The abbey was founded by David the First in 1136 and built from designs by John Moreau, an architect from Paris. In some of the earlier structures blocks of agglomerate from the large quarry of Chiefswood were used but in later buildings, according to the researches of MacGregor and Eckford (1948), stones appear to have been obtained from quarries in the Upper Old Red Sandstone at Ploughlands, near Maxton, $5\frac{1}{2}$ miles E.S.E. of Melrose, and perhaps from St. Boswells Green.

1. Chiefswood Volcanic Neck: Agglomerate

To reach this locality buses proceed from Melrose for a quarter of a mile on the west-going road then turn left into Huntley Road and travel as far as the cemetery (see route-map). At this turning point for the bus the party has only a short walk on a farm-road which passes under the railway and leads up to the quarry.

The north-east margin of this great vent lies close to the south-west of Melrose. The ground plan of the vent is roughly elliptical in form, the long and short diametric distances being

$1\frac{2}{3}$ and $\frac{2}{3}$ mile respectively, and it stretches away from Melrose towards the south-west. The best exposure of the agglomerate filling the vent is in the large quarry in Quarry Hill which overlooks the town. Though now disused this quarry appears to have been in operation from time to time for over 800 years.

The massive vertical walls of agglomerate exposed here and standing to a height of over 100 ft. are most impressive. The face is cut by large vertical joints and there is some evidence of stratification in the form of thick beds dipping inwards from the margin of the vent. The rock when clean weathers to a warm yellowish-brown tone but there is considerable red-staining on the faces. The matrix consists of fragmental material of a light-greenish colour, rough but compact in texture. The larger inclusions, which measure up to 9 in. across, are generally sub-angular or rounded and include such rocks as pink quartz-porphyry and trachytes, grey and purplish basalts, greywacke, shale and reddish sandstone. The inclusions of trachyte, which resemble some of the trachytes of the Eildons, suggest that the vent may have cut through some of these intrusions now removed by denudation.

Although the quarry is situated near the margin of the vent no contacts are seen with the country-rock of Silurian strata but exposed junctions of this kind occur in the near-by Rhymer's Glen. Red sandstones and marls of Upper Old Red age, with some small felsitic intrusions, form a narrow strip bordering the vent-agglomerate on the south side of Quarry Hill. Near Chiefswood House, situated near the centre of the area of the vent, the agglomerate is cut by a quartz-porphyry dyke. It is probable that this large vent and other smaller orifices in the district, at Faldonside, Little Hill and Bowden-moor, originated during the great period of vulcanicity which began in the south of Scotland in late Upper Old Red Sand-stone times and reached a maximum of activity in the Lower Carboniferous. It is remarkable that no plug has so far been found in the Chiefswood vent and it is a matter for speculation

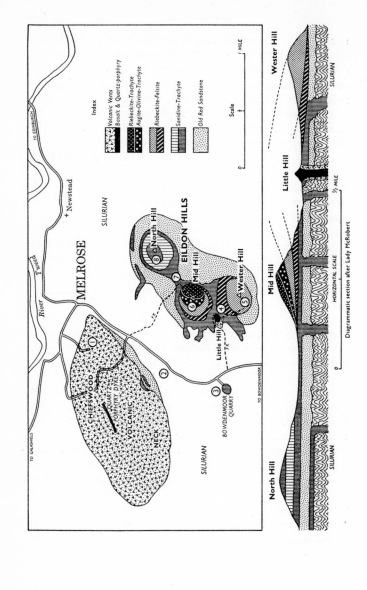

Index

- Volcanic Vents
- Basalt & Quartz-porphyry
- Riebeckite-Trachyte
- Augite-Olivine-Trachyte
- Riebeckite-Felsite
- Sanidine-Trachyte
- Old Red Sandstone

Scale

0 — 1 MILE

TO GALASHIELS

TO EDINBURGH

River Tweed

MELROSE

+ Newstead

SILURIAN

EILDON HILLS

North Hill ⑧

Mid Hill ⑦

⑥

④ ⑤ Wester Hill

Little Hill

CHIEFSWOOD

VOLCANIC NECK

QUARTZ PORPHYRY DYKE

SILURIAN

① ② ③

BOWDENMOOR QUARRY

TO BOWDENMOOR

North Hill

Mid Hill

Little Hill

Wester Hill

SILURIAN

SILURIAN

0   ½ MILE

HORIZONTAL SCALE

Diagrammatic section after Lady McRobert

whether or not lava was ever ejected from this or any of the vents referred to here.

2. Melrose-Bowdenmoor Road South of Chiefswood: Viewpoint for Eildon Hills

On rejoining the bus the road going west to the village of Darnick should be followed, but just before reaching this hamlet the route turns to the left into Chiefswood Road. It now winds along the margin of a high-level terrace of Tweed alluvium by Harleyburn, then rises rather steeply and passes an old quarry in agglomerate to join the main Melrose-Bowden road on the south side of Quarry Hill. From the bus, travelling south-westwards to Bowdenmoor Quarry, the Eildon panorama of hills is in full view. Away to the north-east lies the Black Hill of Earlston, easily distinguished by its fine outline and prominence. The North and Mid hills form the middle foreground, the latter clad in heather and much loose reddish scree. Little Hill is prominent in the valley between Mid Hill and the long heather-clad slopes of Wester Hill, whose steeper sides lie towards Bowden and away from this viewpoint. The foreground is largely covered by boulder clay and the final ice-movement along this part of the broad Tweed basin was from south-west to north-east; drumlins and crag-and-tail ridges are numerous. On the sheltered eastern side of the Eildon Hills boulder clay lies to a height of about 1000 ft. in places. Exposures of the country-rock occur mainly in stream-courses and gullies and show folded greywackes, grits and shales which have been assigned to the Llandovery division of the Silurian. These rocks are generally stained red, a coloration considered to have been derived from overlying red sedimentary rocks long removed by denudation. Only a few relatively small areas of rocks of the Upper Old Red Sandstone are preserved in the district and they lie unconformably on the folded Silurian sediments. These outliers of the Old Red Sandstone owe their preservation to the protection afforded by more resistant igneous rocks which have been intruded into them. This phenomenon is exemplified in the structure of the Eildons where sheets of trachyte and felsite, perhaps in the form of a composite laccolite, have preserved a pedestal of some 300 ft. of strata of the Upper Old Red Sandstone. The basal layer of intrusive rock is a porphyritic sanidine-trachyte which outcrops irregularly around the North and Mid hills about the 1000- and 1100-ft. contour levels. Low on the west side of Mid Hill are three tongues of this basal trachyte which cut across the pedestal of Old Red Sandstone and pass into the underlying Silurian rocks about the 700-ft. level. They have been regarded as portions of feeder-dykes centrally situated beneath the laccolite; the acid sheets of the Eildons may thus represent only a part of the eastern half of the original intrusion. Reference may be made here to the occurrence of the relatively rare mineral riebeckite, which occurs in certain of the trachytic and felsitic rocks. It was first discovered by Professor Bonney in 1882 in granite from Socotra. In 1887 Professor Sauer of Leipzig examined rocks from Socotra collected by Dr Riebeck and detected a blue mineral in them, which he referred to the amphiboles and named 'riebeckite'. In 1891 the mineral was recognized by Teall in rocks from Ailsa Craig. Barron, in 1896, discovered it in the trachytes of the Black Hill of Earlston and in Eildon Mid Hill, making the first record of its occurrence on the mainland of Scotland.

3. Bowdenmoor Quarry: Sanidine-trachyte and Inclusions

Bowdenmoor Quarry lies about 150 yd. west of the Melrose-Bowden road. It has been developed for road metal in an isolated mass of sanidine-trachyte and is, roughly, circular in plan. The trachyte has been quarried on two levels, the lower, about 8 ft. in height, forms a bench 20 yd. wide against the back or south sector. The overall height of the face in part of the east sector is about 50 ft. Lady McRobert described the rock, as, 'a fine-grained, pink, compact trachyte, showing scattered small sanidine-phenocrysts, generally decomposed. These lie in a trachytic ground-mass of sanidine-laths, with a certain amount of primary interstitial quartz; sometimes enclosing the laths ophitically. The rock, as a whole resembles the trachyte of the spur extending westwards from Eildon Wester Hill' (McRobert 1914, p. 310). Bowdenmoor Quarry is remarkable in that four relatively large masses of sedimentary rocks are seen enclosed or involved in the trachyte. One of these masses is conspicuous in the central part of the quarry, having been left by the quarrymen as unsuitable material. It is in the form of a ridge and consists of some 12 ft. of almost vertical beds of hardened and shattered sandstone, conglomerate and mudstone, all with considerable earthy hæmatite in patches and cavities. The length of the mass is about 40 ft., measured along the strike, which runs roughly N.E. Another smaller and more broken mass of similar strata occurs in the north-west part of the quarry. Patches of chilled trachyte still adhere to these sediments which are altered and coloured green near the contacts. In the south face some 12 ft. of beds of purplish and greenish mudstones, with rough sandstone bands, are clearly 'floated' as a mass in the trachyte. The length of this mass is about 30 ft. and the bedding is regular with a gentle dip towards the west. A similar mass of mudstone lies in the trachyte a short distance to the right or west of the last mentioned mass but is less well-defined owing to talus. These enclosed masses are composed of types of sediments common to the Upper Old Red Sandstone and they may have been split off and carried along by the molten trachyte-sheet. This outlier of sanidine-trachyte may be a remnant of the basal western part of the Eildon laccolite.

On joining the main road the route enters the field on the east side of the road at a farm-gate near the plantation which surrounds a small reservoir. From this point an overgrown footpath leads eastwards over a dome of boulder clay and by two wicket-gates to the base of Little Hill (see guide-map).

4. Little Hill: Basalt Plug and Agglomerate in Volcanic Neck

This conspicuous, though small, hill is a volcanic neck com-posed of agglomerate with two kinds of intruded basalt form-ing a plug. The rocks are stained red and contact junctions are not well-defined. The main basalt is a fine-grained non-porphyritic type and occurs around the craggy summit area, while a lower craggy hill at the west side is composed of a Markle type basalt with large and well-defined phenocrysts of labradorite. Agglomerate occurs in contact with this basalt and it is also seen in a small outcrop located in the grass-land south of the western end of the hill. Contacts with sedimentary rocks are not seen. Fine-grained sanidine-trachyte, of the basal Eildon sheet, occurs as a narrow strip on the north side of the hill where it is in contact with red-stained, highly altered platy greywackes and shales. As already stated (p. 103) this vent appears to be of later age than the acid rocks of the Eildons.

5. Wester Hill: Riebeckite-Felsite

The whole of the Wester Hill is composed of riebeckite-felsite which probably occurs in two layers. McRobert (1914, pp. 308–9) states that, 'In the lower layer the rock is pink, with small dark patches of riebeckite. Under the microscope the riebeckite-growths are minute, and largely altered to limonite. In the upper layers the rock is purplish grey, weathering pale pink or white, with conchoidal fracture. Fresh riebeckite is abundant in nests and irregular aggregates.' A good exposure of hard pink felsite with fine vertical jointing, of a columnar type, may be easily reached from Little Hill by following sheep-walks about the 1000-ft. contour to a small quarry 500 yd. to the south-south-east. The felsite of Wester Hill rests partly on Upper Old Red Sandstone rocks and partly on the basal sheet of sanidine-trachyte. It may be noted here that on the west side of the hill the basal sheet of trachyte passes into a feeder-like spur.

6. Mid Hill: Riebeckite-Felsite and Trachyte Sheets

The ascent of Mid Hill is conveniently made from the col between the Mid and Wester hills just east of Little Hill. The lower slopes of the hill are covered by loose scree but from the col a rising traverse bearing to the east should be made for a short distance to a well-defined narrow bench. From this point upwards there are numerous outcrops of riebeckite-felsite, similar to that of Wester Hill, among the scree between the 1100 and 1200-ft. contour levels. A further short traverse to the east side should now be made where good craggy outcrops of orthophyric riebeckite-trachyte occur over the south-east face and continue to the summit of the hill. A sheet of augite-olivine-trachyte lies below the riebeckite-trachyte but this is best seen a short distance west and south-west of the trigonometrical station. The felsites and higher trachyte of Mid Hill have been shown by Lady McRobert in plan and section as wedge-shaped sheets tilted towards the north-east where the wedge-edges of the sheets come successively in contact with the basal sheet of sanidine-trachyte. The same author describes the summit-rocks as follows: 'Two interesting rocks occur towards the top of the Mid Hill. The actual summit consists of orthophyric riebeckite-trachyte, while to the west of this occurs augite-olivine-trachyte. Hand-specimens from the junction can be selected showing the two types intimately mixed.' The cognate xenolith of riebeckite-granite described by Dr J. Phemister (*in* Eckford and Manson, 1928) was collected near this junction. Again, 'The orthophyric riebeckite-trachyte... is a very hard, compact, brown rock with a contorted fluxion-cleavage, recalling in appearance corrugated iron. Riebeckite is conspicuous in blue mossy aggregates. The augite-olivine-trachyte . . . is a very hard, compact, grey-green rock, with good felspar-phenocrysts. It weathers to a buff colour, and has an irregular fracture.'—'This augite-olivine-trachyte closely resembles specimens from Traprain Law and the Bass Rock (East Lothian)', (McRobert, 1914, p. 309).

An indicator on the summit of Mid Hill shows the landmarks and features of interest visible on a fine day. It would be difficult to find a better vantage point from which to view the extensive panorama of the Borderland and feel the magic of its appeal. Sir Walter Scott claimed that he could point out forty-one historic sites from this summit and for him the Eildons were 'the delectable mountains'.

7. Valley between Mid and North hills: Sanidine-Trachyte and Baked Mudstone

From the summit of Mid Hill a steep footpath is followed northwards downhill across much scree to the valley between the Mid and North Hills. In an old quarry near the footpath in the valley a thin bed of hardened mudstone occurs between two sheets of sanidine-trachyte dipping to the west at a fairly high angle. The upper sheet is reddish and shows a chilled basal edge while the top of the lower sheet is rough and spongy. Lady McRobert considered this exposure as part of the basal sheet of sanidine-trachyte connecting the Mid and North hills.

8. North Hill: Varieties of Sanidine-Trachyte

At this point reference may be made to the rocks and structure of North Hill. Lady McRobert has shown that this hill consists almost entirely of three sheets of sanidine-trachyte which give it a stratiform appearance. The lowest and topmost sheets are porphyritic types while the central thicker sheet is mainly non-porphyritic. The lowest sheet lies on the pedestal of Upper Old Red Sandstone. In character it resembles the trachyte of the basal layer as found in other parts of the complex and in Bowdenmoor Quarry. On North Hill the basal trachyte is followed upwards by a thick sheet of non-porphyritic sanidine-trachyte which, in places, contains much quartz. In the upper part of the sheet idiomorphic phenocrysts

Eildon Hills showing, from left to right, Wester, Mid and North Hills. Remnants of large composite laccolite intruded into Upper Old Red Sandstone

of quartz occur which suggest the presence of a sheet of quartz-porphyry but exposures are inadequate to make this certain. The summit sheet is highly porphyritic with pheno-crysts of fresh sanidine and much quartz. Like Barron, Lady McRobert considered that the rocks of North Hill are petro-graphically distinguishable from those of the Mid and Wester hills and that they were part of a subsidiary dome to the lacco-lite. The summit area of North Hill has been successively an Iron Age fort and a Roman signal station and earthwork-remains of these may still be seen.

From the valley between the Mid and North hills the route follows the footpath down to the golf course. At a locality about a third of the way down sandstone is exposed near some mounds of debris. The site is indicated on 1-inch sheet 25 by the word 'Bourjo' in old English lettering and tradition asserts that the Druids performed their sacrificial rites on these mounds. On the other hand it seems more probable that stones were quarried here for building purposes as there are traces of an old roadway leading from the site towards Melrose. After crossing the golf course the bus is joined at the road near the club-house and the homeward journey commenced by pass-ing through Melrose to the Galashiels road. From this road a short way east of Galashiels, Sir Walter Scott, returning from his continental tour in very poor health, stopped his carriage to look on Abbotsford and its beautiful surroundings. A plaque on the wall by the roadside marks the site which has become known as 'The Scott View'. At Galashiels the bus moves into the Edinburgh road, leaving the Tweed valley to follow that of the Gala Water. On the way northwards numerous quarries and road-cuttings expose greywackes and shales of Silurian age. On reaching the Heriot district the route traverses the Ordovician rocks of the Moorfoot-Lammermoor tableland. By Fala Hill and a spectacular glacial overflow channel the way crosses the Southern Upland Fault once more. From Middleton with its limestone quarries and

I

kilns the route lies across the Midlothian basin to Gilmerton and the capital.

REFERENCES

BARRON, T. 1896. On a new British Rock containing Nepheline and Riebeckite. *Geol. Mag.*, Dec. 4, vol. 3, pp. 371–378.

ECKFORD, R. J. A. and ANDERSON, F. W. 1940. Report on the Building-Stones used in the Construction of the Abbey of St Mary at Melrose. *Hist. Berwickshire Nat. Club*, vol. 30, pp. 178–182.

ECKFORD, R. J. A. and MANSON, W. 1928. Note on a Xenolith in Riebeckite-trachyte, Mid Eildon, Roxburghshire. *Trans. Edin. Geol. Soc.*, vol. 12, part 1, pp. 143–146.

MACGREGOR, A. G. and ECKFORD, R. J. A. 1948. The Upper Old Red and Lower Carboniferous Sediments of Teviotdale and Tweedside, and the Stones of the Abbeys of the Scottish Borderland. *Trans. Edin. Geol. Soc.*, vol. 14, part ii, pp. 230–250.

McROBERT, (Lady) RACHEL W. 1914. Acid and Intermediate Intrusions and Associated Ash-Necks in the Neighbourhood of Melrose (Roxburghshire). *Quart. Journ. Geol. Soc.*, vol. 70, pp. 303–315.

PRINGLE, J. 1948. The South of Scotland. 2nd edit., *British Regional Geology, Geol. Surv.*, pp. 65–70.

R. J. A. ECKFORD AND W. MANSON

MIDDLETON and HERIOT

O.S. One-inch Map, Seventh Series, Sheet 62
G.S. One-inch Maps, Sheets 24, 25 and 32 (Scotland)
Route maps pp. 116, 120

—

PRIVATE transport is desirable if the whole of the suggested excursion is to be covered, but public transport is available along the main Edinburgh-Galashiels route (A.7) and can be used for access to the quarries at Middleton, Hazelbank and Bower (1, 9 & 10). Walking distance is negligible for all exposures are at the roadside with the exception of the Broadlaw Granite, and this is only half-a-mile from the road. This excursion is designed to show a variety of rock types (Carboniferous limestones and shales, granite, Lower Palaeozoic greywackes, shales, cherts and tuffs) and their associated structures; it allows of some good fossil collecting varying from abundant Carboniferous forms to rarer Silurian graptolites; and it affords an excellent opportunity for the appreciation of the geological control over the local topography.

Leaving Edinburgh via the A.7, a traverse is made obliquely across the Midlothian Coal Basin through Newtongrange. At the crossroads in the village of North Middleton turn right on to the C-class road which leads south-westwards to the mine and quarries in the North Greens Limestone. The mining of the limestone has recently been abandoned, but the workings may be inspected under guidance, and it is of interest to see the method which was used in the extraction of the rock. Known as 'pillar and stall' or 'stoop and room', this involved

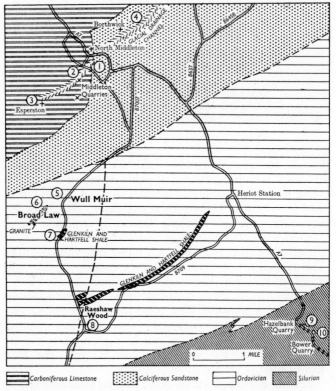

Carboniferous Limestone   Calciferous Sandstone   Ordovician   Silurian

the removal of large masses of the limestone leaving pillars at regular intervals to support the roof.

The North Greens Limestone occurs near the base of the Lower Limestone Group and is of abnormal thickness. Facies changes and some faulting have resulted in the thinning of intervening strata and the coalescing of several limestones. Thus the local equivalents of the Gilmerton, North Greens and Bilston Burn limestones are in close proximity.

1. North Middleton Burn: North Greens Limestone

The North Greens Limestone itself is locally about 50 ft. in thickness and can be seen in exposures in the North Middleton Burn. Crinoidal and coralline limestones occur here together with occasional ribs of chert, but the rocks are best examined in the quarry (356585) immediately south of the lime kilns (the 'old quarry' of Peach *et al.*, 1910, p. 187).

2. North Middleton Quarry: North Greens Limestone

The beds in the quarry dip at 12° to the north-west and the lower strata consist of compact cream or pale grey limestone. The rock is dominantly clastic, being made up of whole or fragmented shells. Corals, brachiopods and crinoids may easily be seen but are extracted only with difficulty. Better collecting is afforded by the top 12 ft. of the limestone which are accessible in the south of the quarry. Soft, calcareous shales are here developed between thin (6 in. to 1 ft.) nodular limestone bands and a varied fauna may be rapidly obtained. The forms which occur most commonly are *Zaphrentis*, *Caninia*, *Dibunophyllum*, *Lithostrotion*, *Syringopora*, *Spirifer* and *Productus*. Gastropods and lamellibranchs may also be found; crinoid ossicles are abundant throughout and there are occasional bands especially rich in giganteid Productids. Further details of the fauna are given by Peach *et al* (1910, Appendix B, pp. 384–405).

Before leaving the quarry, it is interesting to observe the fluvio-glacial sands and gravels which form an overburden of up to 30 ft. in thickness above the limestone. The deposits are associated with the important Borthwick glacial drainage channel. The Middleton North Burn occupies the upper reaches of this channel but it is a much more pronounced feature a mile or so to the north-east (Kendall and Bailey, 1908).

3. Esperston Quarry: Limestone

Those who have an especial interest in Carboniferous limestones and their faunas may wish to spend additional time (at the expense of other localities) examining the exposures in the North Greens Limestone in the large quarry (the 'New' Middleton Quarry of Peach *et al.* 1910, p. 187) to the south (355575). In addition the Esperston quarry which lies about a mile to the west (343570) may be visited. They afford exposures of the local equivalent of the Bilston Burn Limestone.

4. Borthwick: Glacial Drainage Channel

The main road (A.7) should be rejoined at North Middleton where the drainage channel can be seen running through the village and past Borthwick church. After about a mile and a half the right turn should be taken along the road B.7007. This road runs over flat, low-lying land formed by the soft sediments of the Calciferous Sandstone measures, south towards the Southern Upland Fault. The fault itself is not exposed, but the resistant Ordovician greywackes on the south side have formed a very prominent scarp feature which is especially impressive on this particular approach.

5. Viewpoint: Wull Muir

The road curves away to the south-east just on the line of the fault and climbs obliquely up the scarp for some 300 ft. When the top is reached advantage should be taken of the very fine view over this part of the Midland Valley. In the foreground, as already noted, the Calciferous Sandstone forms low monotonous country. This becomes more varied to the north and west where the Lower Limestone Group appears; beyond, the lines of bings indicate the outcrops of the Limestone Coal Group (Edge Coals) and the Productive Coal Measures. In the distance, beyond the great Pentland Fault, the Pentland Hills, composed of Old Red Sandstone and Silurian rocks, rise up from the Carboniferous sediments. A marked difference can be seen between the topographic expression of the lavas and that of the sediments of Old Red Sandstone age, and from this distance, the softer rounded sandstone hills in the south contrast with the higher, steep-sided hills of lavas to the north. The range falls in height towards the north-east and the city of Edinburgh, where the Castle Rock can be seen. To the right Salisbury Craigs forms a prominent scarp feature and leads to the volcanic mass of Arthur's Seat. Under favourable circumstances the view stretches right across the Firth to Fife and with very favourable conditions to the Ochil Hills, another range of Old Red Sandstone lavas.

6. Broadlaw Granite

The Broadlaw 'Granite' is found about half-a-mile to the west of the road at the top of the scarp. It consists of a small mass of granodiorite of Caledonian age, no more than half-a-mile in length and about 100 yd. at its maximum width. Elongated in a north-easterly direction, it has been intruded into and approximately along the strike of the surrounding Ordovician rocks. The contact of the granodiorite with the sediments is nowhere exposed, though Mould (1947) reports a small roadside exposure in hornfelsed mudstones and greywackes.

The grandiorite of the main quarry is grey in colour except for the rock in the south-east corner which is red. Both varieties consist essentially of quartz, plagioclase and orthoclase feldspar, and biotite; accessory minerals include zircon, apatite and pyrite. In the grey rock the texture is porphyritic, the phenocrysts of plagioclase (oligoclase with cores of labradorite) being set in a finer-grained matrix. The brown biotite is usually altered to chlorite. The red granodiorite has an even medium-grained texture and as a whole it is slightly more acid. The plagioclase is slightly more sodic than that of the grey variety and is generally sericitized.

Baked shales and mudstones are found as small xenoliths and in some cases a hornfels has been formed consisting of quartz, the andesine variety of plagioclase and biotite. Mould

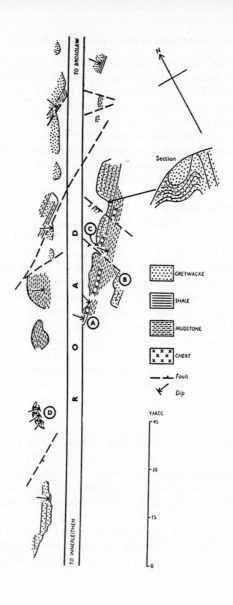

N

TO BROADLAW

Section

ROAD

C

B

A

D

GREYWACKE

SHALE

MUDSTONE

X X X
X X X CHERT

— ·· — Fault

↙ Dip

YARDS

45

30

15

0

TO INNERLEITHEN

(1947) also reports the occurrence of hornblende, actinolite, corundum and, rarely, of sillimanite in the xenoliths.

Jointing is well-developed and a number of lines of shearing and crushing can be seen in the quarry. Veins of quartz are fairly common and other thin veins are filled with pyrite and arsenopyrite.

The main grandiorite is surrounded by a fine-grained quartz diorite which is poorly exposed to the north-east of the main quarry.

7. Broadlaw; 'Arenig Inlier' (Map p. 120)

An inlier of supposed Arenig cherts with overlying graptolitic shales has been described by Peach and Horne (1899, p. 269) lying half-a-mile south of the granodiorite. The rocks are exposed on both sides of the road for about 200 yd. and, according to Peach and Horne, consist of black radiolarian cherts followed by grey mudstones with black shale seams which are overlain by a band of black shales. This shale band is succeeded in turn by greywackes with black shale partings. The grey mudstones above the cherts were thought to be Glenkiln in age while the black shale band and the greywacke succession above, which yielded *Diplograptus foliaceus, Lasiograptus margaritatus* and *Dicellograptus* were interpreted as being of Hartfell age.

The rocks currently exposed are represented on the map on p. 120. Some faulting and slight folding are readily seen but the presence of an anticline cannot be demonstrated. The exposures are however sufficient to demonstrate clearly that the black chert bands are not confined to one horizon in the core of the supposed fold. The best exposure of chert is at point *A* where 4 ft. of this rock may be seen. It is dominantly black and occurs in bands or lenses up to 3 or 4 in. in thickness which are separated by very pale greenish-grey, soft mudstone partings. The chert bands themselves may become very pale grey in colour towards their margins.

Pale grey mudstones with black shales underlie the cherts in the same exposure (the rocks are probably inverted, the mudstones being younger than the cherts in this exposure). The mudstones are hard, blocky and pale grey when fresh, weathering to a mottled brown and yellow appearance. The fresh grey surface often has a brecciated appearance with patches of differing grey colours and sometimes large aggregates of pyrite. Some bands are coarser in grain and ashy in composition (C on map p. 120). North of the fault at B the grey mudstones are in normal contact with greywackes and shales and it is of particular significance that thin but undoubted bands (about 1 in. in thickness) of chert occur within the shales. Furthermore thin black chert bands are also found in the grey mudstones on the north-west side of the road at point D. It seems clear that the chert is of Glenkiln age and interbedded with the other sediments rather than being of an entirely different, Arenig, age. In this respect it is of interest to note that ashy bands and radiolarian cherts occur in the Glenkiln rocks of the Moffat region (e.g. Peach and Horne, 1899, p. 103).

Southwards the route runs through country which is typical of the Southern Uplands and is characterized by well-rounded moorland with more or less constant summit levels and deeply incised streams with flat valley floors. A small overflow channel may be observed on the north side of the road (352523) and, if desired, a further opportunity for the study of the cherts and graptolitic shales is provided in the exposures opposite Garvald farmhouse (354513). No fossils have been reported from this locality, however, and the best exposures are situated some 200 yd. up the hillside.

8. Raeshaw Wood Quarry: Caradoc Sediments

Strongly jointed, pebbly greywackes and siltstones are found in a large roadside (B.709) quarry at Raeshaw Wood. The coarse-grained rocks are made up of a variety of rock

fragments, quartz grains and large floats of black shale set in a
fine-grained matrix of clay. The shale fragments have yielded
a number of graptolites (*Climacograptus scharenbergi*, *C.*
bicornis, *Cryptograptus tricornis*, *Dicellograptus* and *Didymo-*
graptus superstes—Peach and Horne 1899, p. 270). This evidence
points to the erosion of the underlying shales by strong currents bringing along the detritus which formed the pebble
beds. Although the rocks are highly inclined their way-up may
be deduced from the grading which occurs in the greywackes.

This detection of upward stratigraphic sequence is of the
utmost importance in rocks of this type which have undergone
severe folding, and grading is only one of a number of features
which can be used. Other sedimentary structures which are
valuable in this respect can be seen in the last two localities to
be visited on this excursion—the quarries at Hazelbank and
Bower.

9. Hazelbank Quarry: Silurian Sediments

The road eastwards from Ladyside leads to Heriot Station
and the A.7 road. Hazelbank Quarry (426506) lies on this road
about $3\frac{1}{2}$ ml. south of the station and exposes greywackes and
intervening beds of shale and siltstone which dip at 70°–90°
towards the east-south-east. The rocks are strongly jointed and
cut by a number of small normal and reverse faults. Grading in
the greywackes suggests that the beds young eastwards and
this is confirmed by the small-scale cross-bedding present in the
ripple-marked siltstones. The flute, groove and longitudinal-
ripple casts present on the under-surfaces of the greywackes
also indicate the way-up. Fragmentary graptolites may be
obtained from one of the thicker bands of siltstone and shale
exposed towards the southern corner of the quarry.

10. Bower Quarry: Silurian Sediments

Graptolites have also been reported from the quarry at
Bower, about 500 yd. south of Hazelbank. Thus Peach and

Horne (1899, p. 194) record the presence of *Climacograptus normalis, Diplograptus* and a number of fragments which are taken to indicate a horizon in the zone of *Akidograptus acuminatus*, that is at the base of the Birkhill succession. This means that the great thickness of greywackes and fine-grained beds in the present region is laterally equivalent to the thin black shales of Dobb's Linn and Moffatdale (Excursion pp. 144). It is evident that the dying out of the sandy detritus with concomitant thinning of the succession took place towards the axis of the geosyncline in Lower Silurian times. This has led to the suggestion of the presence of a land mass lying to the north-west, and measurement of the orientation of ripple marks and sole structures confirms that the Silurian currents flowed from this direction.

Interest also attaches to the fact that the sedimentary features developed in the rocks at Bower indicate that the beds, dipping at 85° towards the north-west, are the right way up. This can in fact be appreciated immediately on entering the quarry for many of the bedding planes display well-developed transverse- and interference-ripple marks characteristic of the upper surfaces of greywacke beds. Clearly, a synclinal axis must lie in the unexposed ground between the two quarries.

The greywackes in the two quarries are different in colour, but this is due to secondary staining. The Hazelbank rocks are a pale greenish-grey whereas those of Bower have been distinctly reddened by iron oxides (mostly haematite). This reddening is presumably related to the presence of Old Red Sandstones which must have overlain the Silurian rocks. All the greywackes have essentially the same texture and composition with the larger constituents set in a clay matrix. Of the larger particles, quartz and feldspar are present along with rock fragments of granite, quartz porphyry and keratophyre, spilite and andesite, shale and red mudstone or chert and an occasional mica or chlorite schist. It is suggested above that the parent land mass of the sediments lay towards the north and west of the present outcrops; the composition of the fragments suggests further that this land mass was made up largely of lower Ordovician volcanic and sedimentary rocks associated with a mass of granite and some metamorphic rocks.

The direct return to Edinburgh is made through Newton-grange and Eskbank on the road A.7.

REFERENCES

KENDALL, P. F. and BAILEY, E. B., 1908. The glaciation of East Lothian south of the Garleton Hills. *Trans. Roy. Soc. Edinburgh*, vol. 46, pp. 1–31.

MOULD, D. D. C. P., 1947. The Broadlaw 'Granite'. *Geol. Mag.*, vol. 84, pp. 178–180.

PEACH, B. N. *et al.*, 1910. The Geology of the Neighbour-hood of Edinburgh. 2nd edit. *Mem. Geol. Surv.*

PEACH, B. N. and HORNE, J., 1899. The Silurian rocks of Britain, vol. 1 Scotland. *Mem. Geol. Surv.*

TULLOCH, W. and WALTON, H. S., 1958. The Geology of the Midlothian Coalfield. *Mem. Geol. Surv.*

E. K. WALTON

EDDLESTON GRAVEL-MORAINE

O.S. One-inch Map, Seventh Series, Sheets 62 and 69
G.S. One-inch Map, Sheet 24 (Scotland), Drift Edition
Route-map p. 128

◆

EDDLESTON village lies seventeen miles south of Edinburgh
and four miles north of Peebles. This excursion is described on
the presumption that a geological party from Edinburgh will
travel by private transport. Leadburn provides a convenient
landmark, for just beyond it the road enters the area shown on
the route-map. To the south it then follows with two diver-
sions, the Eddleston valley as far as the village. Here, after
turning sharply into a side road on the right and crossing the
railway at the station, it climbs up into the Meldon valley. The
return journey may be varied according to choice. It is, however, possible to replan the excursion so as to use public transport, travelling from Edinburgh by rail or road to Eddleston.
The bus in particular, follows the Leadburn-Eddleston-Peebles
road along the Eddleston valley. Only strong walkers will
complete the programme in a whole day.

The object of the excursion is to examine a belt of glacial
gravel which extends, almost without interruption, for six
miles along the Eddleston valley (five of them above the village), then three miles along the Meldon valley, and finally up
the Tweed valley beyond Stobo into ground not shown on
the route-map. It is considered probable, though not certain,
that the gravels of this belt constitute a natural unit, a gravel-
moraine supplied by a glacier which stood to the west and

north-west. This view is supported by a number of observations:

(1) The main Eddleston gravels are valley-side gravels dis-
posed in hummocks and ridges and occasionally associated
with kettle-holes. The ridges are typical kames and run approximately north and south; they are restricted almost wholly
to the west slope of the valley, where they are at present being
extensively excavated. Their tumultous bedding, thus brought
to light, predominantly dips steeply to the east. This leads to
the conclusion that the gravels were delivered by transient
torrents coming from the west, from a glacier the top of which
stood at some higher level.

(2) Supplementary suggestive evidence of delivery from the
west is furnished just across the valley from Eddleston at the
Black Barony Hotel (Darn Hall). It depends on external deltaic
form rather than on exposure of internal bedding.

(3) The Eddleston valley-side gravels are certainly a con-
temporary, natural series in their course from the head of the
valley to the point, rather more than a mile south of the village, beyond which, as far as Eddleston valley is concerned,
they fail completely. It is true that the route-map shows some
glacial gravel further downstream, especially near Peebles, but
this is a valley-bottom deposit, very different from the valley-
side gravel with which we are concerned. What is shown in
black as alluvium in this map is almost certainly in large
measure valley-bottom glacial gravel, more or less reworked;
and what is shown as glacial gravel in the Eddleston valley
towards Peebles behaves as a low terrace above this alluvium.

(4) As the Eddleston valley-side gravels are almost restricted
to the west side of the valley, it is suggested by one of us
(E.B.B.) that the glacier which deposited them had been
halted by a torrent developed in successive summers along the
bottom of this valley.

(5) In keeping, it is further suggested that the Eddleston
valley-side gravels do not continue into the last three miles of

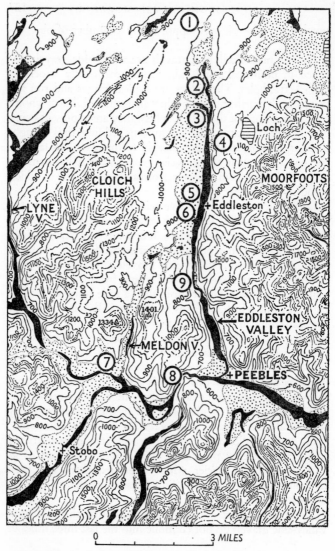

Black, 'alluvium'; dots, glacial gravel; blank, boulder clay and rock.
Geology after Geological Survey, Contours after Ordnance Survey.

the Eddleston valley *because* the glacier responsible for them was, in this part of its course, halted at the Meldon valley to the west. Here are found gravels that we take to be essentially the southward continuation of the Eddleston valley-side gravels. Again, one notices a tendency for the gravels to concentrate on the west side of the valley.

(6) On approaching the Tweed, down the Meldon valley, complications are introduced owing to important valley-bottom terraces of glacial gravel developed along both the Lyne and the Tweed. This leads to a gap in kame-featuring between the Meldon and the Tweed; but the gap is only half a mile wide, and the ridges either side are aligned. The Tweed kames are strongly marked immediately south of the Lyne half a mile upstream from its junction with the Tweed.

Details of Excursion

It is suggested that preliminary notice should be given for Cowieslinn Quarry to W. & J. R. Watson Ltd., Romano House, Station Road, Corstorphine, and for Shiphorn Quarry to Shiphorn Estates Ltd., Eddleston, and that the party should be suitably shod for muddy patches.

1. Northern End of Eddleston Gravels

If the party leaves Edinburgh at 2 p.m. it should, by 2.30 p.m., be about three-quarters of a mile south of Leadburn at a bend of the road carrying the ninth milestone from Peebles. A little to the east, the party will here recognize the most northerly mound of the Eddleston gravels. This and the neighbouring mounds can be looked at without stopping.

2. Cowieslinn Quarry

A mile beyond this, at the eighth milestone from Peebles, the alluvium of the Eddleston valley commences (shown in black on route-map), and a full half-mile farther on it turns for a little from south-south-east to south-south-west. The

K

Middleton Quarry showing workings in North Greens Limestone

main road follows the alluvium and, just before reaching this bend, is joined by a branch road leading to Nether Fala farm, a prominent building to the west set among trees on a mound. The party should turn up this branch road, marked by a sign-post 'Cowieslinn Quarry', and continue to just north of the farm. Here they must dismount and take another branch road at right angles, which leads to the most northerly and smallest of the presently worked gravel pits. If a bus is employed it can meanwhile continue to the main pit, where there is ample turning space once across the railway, and it can wait till rejoined.

At the minor pit (as elsewhere) the party will note that the gravel is made of a mixture of stones, some well water-worn, others merely blunted, along with a plentiful matrix of impure loamy sand. Among the stones local rocks, namely early-Palæozoic greywacke, shale and chert, abound; sandstones, lavas and felsites of Lower Old Red Sandstone types are easy to find, while coal and schist seem to be absent. The early-Palæozoic rocks, so far as character is concerned, might have come from any direction; the Old Red sandstones and lavas come from some part of an extensive belt to the west; only the felsites, which are of Tinto type, can be assigned to a restricted source. Tinto lies twenty miles west-south-west of Eddleston, but the distribution of its felsite in drift covers a considerable area.

The bedding of the gravel and associated sand is extremely complex. The question which seems to deserve most attention is whether or not a steep dip towards the east is sufficiently predominant to justify the view, advanced by the authors, that the gravel has been tipped from the upper portion of a glacier standing on the west.

It is well to walk along the foot of the gravel face and return by the top, but to remember that the main Cowieslinn pit should be left at 4 p.m.

The main pit repeats the opportunities for examination that

are afforded in the minor pit. Here again, after studying the sections from the floor of the pit, a return should be made, if time allows, along the top.

3. Shiphorn Quarry

At 4 p.m. the party should regain the main road, and follow it once more south towards Eddleston. Shortly after passing the seventh milestone from Peebles, the main road is crossed by a branch road coming from Temple and Gorebridge. Turn south-west along this branch road, which is marked with a sign-post 'Shiphorn Quarry'. Continue until the railway is passed, when the party can dismount, and the bus turn and wait.

From this point, which lies just south of the important tributary alluvium shown on the route-map, two roads lead into the gravel pit. The lower closely follows the railway; the upper is the one for the party, which will take it on foot. At present (1959) it gives very easy access to the top of the most conspicuous kame of the whole district, with accompanying kettle-holes. The top of this kame stands 860 ft. above sea-level, 140 ft. higher, that is, than the valley-bottom alluvium of the Eddleston Water along its foot. Return can be made at various levels on the floor of the pit. The phenomena are as seen in the previous pits, with occasional slight folding such as may be ascribed to glacial push.

Rejoining the bus not later than 4.45 p.m., the party will return to the main road to travel south again. Beyond the gravel pit just visited, a continuation of the conspicuous kame locally shows predominant eastward dip where eaten into by the Eddleston Water; this can be seen in passing.

4. Gravel Pit 1½ miles North of Eddleston

The next stop should be a mile south of the Shiphorn Quarry road, opposite a solitary pine growing on the alluvium. Here a gravel pit, just east of the road, once more shows steep east-ward dip. There is no need to dismount.

5. Black Barony Hotel (Darn Hall): Delta

Another brief halt without dismounting should be made a few yards before the first houses of Eddleston, which will allow the party to look up a lime avenue leading to the Black Barony Hotel (Darn Hall) across the valley. The lime trees are planted on the upper member of a specially interesting double delta, best studied if the party has arranged tea at the hotel. At any rate, the bus must turn right at Eddleston along the branch road leading up to the Meldon valley.

Across the railway, halt at the gate to the modern drive of the hotel. Like the lime avenue this drive is on the upper, steep member of the Black Barony double delta. Below it, bordering an important tributary stream, is a much lower, flatter member. The original, upper delta was built when the stream was overloaded with gravel and it is tempting to think of it as contemporaneous with the still steeper-faced kames, but dumped by a more persistent current. The great erosion accompanying the formation of the lower delta was evidently performed by the same stream when supplied with less to carry—presumably when the glacier had melted back.

If the party goes up to the hotel it must not be misled by artificial trimming of the upper delta above the termination of the lime avenue.

The remainder of the excursion is a bus run: up to and along the Meldon valley; south-west to cross the Lyne above Sheriffmuir, half a mile upstream from the junction of Lyne and Tweed; down the Tweed past Neidpath Castle to Peebles; and so home by Eddleston.

What is seen can be gathered from paragraphs 5 and 6 of our introductory remarks. Here there is only space to mention four particulars:

6. Kaim Rig

Half a mile south-west of the hotel gate, the road passes

Huttonknowe farm; alongside is a conspicuous kame called Kaim Rig.

7. Tweed Kames

The south-west road skirting Sheriffmuir, between Lyne and Tweed, has well-developed Tweed kames to the north-west. These differ strikingly from the fluvioglacial terrace-gravels which floor the moor and extend downstream to the loop of the Tweed two miles south-west of Peebles.

8. Neidpath Gorge

The Neidpath gorge beyond the loop presents a problem quite unconnected with the subject of our excursion, but very impressive. Many think this gorge was cut by a tributary of the Tweed, thus short-circuiting a previous great meander of the main river. A four-mile deserted stretch of this hypo-thetical meander leaves the Manor valley three miles south-west of Peebles, and can be clearly recognized in the route-map as a long narrow gap in the 700-ft. contour. If desired this route can be taken to Peebles instead of passing Neidpath. To do so, cross the Tweed near the second milestone from Peebles, taking the road that leads through Mill Kirkton and Hallyard.

9. Lower Eddleston Valley

The absence of valley-side gravels in the lowest three miles of the Eddleston valley can be realized from the nature of the topography.

REFERENCES

BAILEY, E. B., and ECKFORD, R. J. A., 1956. Eddleston Gravel-Moraine. *Trans. Edin. Geol. Soc.*, vol. 16, pp. 254–261.

E. B. BAILEY AND R. J. A. ECKFORD

NOBLE HOUSE, LAMANCHA

O.S. One-inch Map, Edinburgh, Seventh Series, Sheet 74
G.S. One-inch Map, Peebles, Sheet 24 (Scotland)
Route map p. 136

THE structure of the Noble House area is that of a west-south-west to east-north-east anticline of siltstones and greywackes including the 'Haggis Rock', covering a core of Llandeilo sediments and igneous layers. These beds are truncated west-wards by the Southern Upland Boundary Fault which is reversed by pressure from the south-east. On its north-west side there are good exposures of Lower Old Red Sandstone. One of these is in a conglomerate with andesite boulders up to nine inches in diameter, seen in Burn E.

Noble House may be reached from Edinburgh by public transport (Scottish Omnibuses Ltd., Edinburgh–Moffat via Leadburn). The excursion should start from Noble House, an old posting station celebrated by Sir Walter Scott at the beginning of '*Redgauntlet*'. Here several streams, which have been lettered A to E on the sketch-map, emerge from small gorges at about the 825-ft. level. This may represent a Pliocene base-level of erosion, probably a coastline.

1. Burn B Noble House: Romanno Greywacke

On the south side of Burn B, south-east of the fence, three small scarps of Romanno Greywacke show evidence of thrusting from the south-east, a point brought out by grey siltstones dipping off the most northerly unit, and by characteristic changes of dip. The type locality (162468) of the

Romanno Greywacke is on the east side of the road at Newlands Kirk, three quarters of a mile south of Romanno Bridge. Characteristically it is a grit with quartz grains, pink-stained albite often in nearly complete angular crystals, garnets sometimes with pieces of quartz-biotite-schist or albite-schist adhering, and small spilite fragments. Keratophyre (=soda trachyte) fragments may occur, but they are relatively rare.

2. *Burn A Noble House: Siltstone, Grit, Chert and Boulder Bed*

The excursion now proceeds to Burn A, where the Romanno Greywacke with its coloured fragments, is succeeded upstream by grey siltstones and grits which are affected by an apparently normal fault throwing down towards north-north-west. There is some slumping in the sandy layers. Immediately to the south-east we reach a gently inclined, dull chert, with films of specular iron-ore in joints and also thin deposits of a shiny black material like an oil residue. This chert has a fauna principally of tiny simple conodonts and has not yet been correlated with other outcrops.

Next, at a little waterfall, comes the Boulder Bed, with rounded blocks up to over a foot in diameter and comprising diabase, red chert, and less frequently silicified dark siltstone. Under the Boulder Bed a small reef of red chert dips south-east off a diabase intrusion. In the latter, coarse stellate groups of plagioclase (oligoclase-andesine) are partly enclosed by augite crystals. There are no vesicles. A few nearly vertical short quartz veins in the diabase trend from west to east.

Across a fault we reach an orange-weathering greywacke striking vertically north-north-east. It is infolded, with north-easterly plunge, in grey and green siltstones which extend for about one eighth of a mile along the gully, before dipping steeply east-south-east under Romanno Greywacke over-thrust from the south-south-east. There follows a thin chert perhaps interstratified in the greywacke. South of another

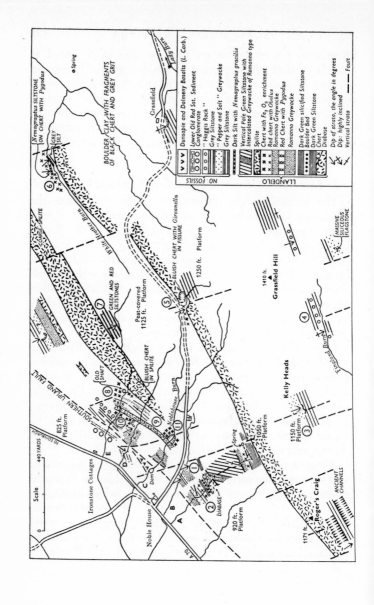

fault comes vertical dark-green silicified siltstone like that associated with the diabase and the Boulder Bed.

3. Kelly Heads Quarry: Greywacke

From the top of Burn A the party may cross the 1050-ft. and 1150-ft. platforms, noting how the higher of these corresponds with the two ancient drainage channels south of the Roger's Craig spilitic ridge, and ascend to Kelly Heads quarry, where there is clear evidence of a small north-north-west fault. In the quarry 'Pepper and Salt' greywacke with abundant fragments of keratophyre from the Tweeddale lavas, dips under grey siltstones.

4. Grassfield Hill and Fingland Burn: 'Haggis Rock'

On Grassfield Hill, there is a platform at 1300 ft. This slopes eastwards to 1250 ft., and is separated by a sharp declivity from the 1150-ft. platform which falls eastwards to not much more than 1100 ft. at Ruddenleys. Soon the head of the Fingland Burn is reached. Almost exactly at the 1250-ft. contour, in a long outcrop of shattery pale-grey siltstones, with irregular calcite veins near a fault, a black and green version of the 'Haggis Rock' occurs with only a few dull red and brown sub-rounded fragments. Pebbles are of chert, quartz-kerato-phyre, spilites with lath arrangements of either intersertal divergent or stellate types, spherulitic and arborescent variolites, and garnet-mica-schist. One mile farther south, near Fingland farmhouse, a similar drab-coloured 'Haggis' (190475) has, in addition, pebbles of epidotized spilite with flow-aligned feldspars, and boulders of brown silty limestone with phyllitic particles, as well as the important hornblende andesite pebbles. Only an energetic party should visit this.

If we keep on south-east of the head of the Fingland Burn, a return is made to 'Pepper and Salt' greywacke. The rock in a small drystane-dyker's quarry is specially hard and siliceous and seems to be on the south limb of a syncline with the 'Haggis Rock' close to the axis.

5. Quarry in Spilite: Girvanella Chert

If we proceed north-north-west from here, over Grassfield Hill, in slightly more than half a mile, we reach a large roadside quarry in vesicular spilite with magnificent pillow structures. Just south of the quarry grey siltstones abut against the spilite, but whether they are overthrust on it or unconformable, it is hard to tell. On the south face of the quarry, an east-north-east trending gash about a foot wide contains an infilling of both crystalline calcite and bluish-green chert. In this chert *Girvanella problematica* Nicholson and Etheridge is found with the two main sizes of calcareous tubules deposited by the algae, just as described from the Stinchar Limestone at Girvan by Professor Alan Wood (1957), but in addition there are small flattened thallus lobes with a suggestion that these may grow from each other as in *Caulerpa* (Siphonales) and indications of paired buds to give rise to the intertwining tubules.

A fault in the burn just west of the main quarry, brings up dull red chert. Close under the spilite junction, this chert is full of chlorite patches reaching a millimetre or two across. In the chlorite chert is an abundance of very small *Obolus*, *Lingula*, and *Paterula*. The conodonts *Periodon* and *Prioniodina* are present but scarce, and there is no trace of *Pygodus*.

6. White Heather Burn: Nemagraptus gracilis and Conodonts

From here we may go on to a graptolite locality (203506) in rapidly alternating dark and light grey siltstone with *Nemagraptus gracilis*, a quarter of a mile south-west of Ruddenleys. This siltstone, on the north side of White Heather Burn, has several species of graptolites including *Climacograptus bicornis* with long 'horns'. The strike is roughly east-west, with steep dip to south, and shows a small transverse fold plunging to the south. Beneath the graptolitic siltstone, lie much-faulted and secondarily reddened cherts with high Llandeilo conodonts and *Lingula* cf. *brevis*. The westernmost outcrop of chert dips obliquely under spilite which appears to be overthrust.

7-8. Burn E upper reaches: Spilite, Chert and Greywacke

If we return westwards, green and red siltstones may be examined in a knoll situated to south of a much larger elongate hill of fine-grained spilite (7). At the west end of this hill, in Burn E, a vesicular spilite has inclusions of calcite and bright-green chlorite and occasional small patches of bluish-green chert. This looks very like the same spilite as that in the *Girvanella* quarry (5), repeated by thrusting.

South of the old shaft (8) which is sunk in iron-enriched, quartz-veined, smashed chert, a hard chert dips to south-south-east under the spilite. The hematite-chert continues downstream further on the north than on the south bank, possibly owing to a north-west fault. On the south bank an outcrop of greywacke intervenes before we reach a block of upended, strongly compressed green siltstones which have small folds plunging north-north-east.

9. Burn D: Greywacke

The greywacke just described may be the same as a vertical Romanno Greywacke bed in the middle of vertical pale green siltstones exposed in Burn D. The greywacke appears to be in normal sedimentary contact with the siltstones in Burn D, and this is strong reason for placing these pale-green siltstones in the same stratigraphical group as the Romanno Greywacke which further west in Burn D also shows intercalation between two beds of chert. These cherts dip fairly gently to south-south-east. Both yield *Pygodus*, but the upper one next the hematite-chert quarry is distinguished by the presence of *Obolus* up to one-half inch long and a great predominance of *Periodon serra* over *P. aculeata*.

10. *Burns D and E: Spilite, Greywacke, Chert and 'Haggis Rock'*

The vertical spilite which intervenes between the Romanno Greywacke and the enriched chert in Burn E, may be roughly in its original stratigraphical position, although it may have the form of a pinched-in anticline. The spilite may be traced to Burn D where the cherts and Romanno Greywacke to west of it may be the same as those to east of it in Burn E. The continuity of the spilite between Burns C, D, and E was checked by a variometer survey, in 1951, by Mr Burnett of the Heriot-Watt College; and it is almost certain that it is an older spilite than those farther east.

Downstream from this spilite in Burn E, 'Haggis Rock', with abundant pebbles of spilite, keratophyre, and hornblende andesite, appears in the north bank. It dips steeply north-west and is followed downstream by grey grits and shaly siltstone without visible mica flakes. This 'Haggis' sequence is strongly faulted, but one may conclude that it is unconformable on the Romanno Greywacke beds which occupy the south bank.

11. *Burn C: Haematite-Chert*

The excursion may conclude at the old quarry and mine in Burn C, a quarter of a mile east-south-east of Noble House. It yielded much of the best haematite-chert, in 1884–6, with up to about 50 per cent Fe_2O_3 content. Rounded overfolds about two feet high can be seen at the south-west corner of the working. These indicate movement from the south-south-east with above them a low-angled thrust plane.

If time permits a visit should also be paid to the important conodont chert, a sixth of a mile north-north-west of Ruddenleys (187502), which is not on the route-map. In spite of a good deal of collecting, this remains the only Peeblesshire locality for *Cordylodus spinatus* (Hadding). About 100 yd. north-east of Ruddenleys, intercalated grit in hard red conodont chert yields fragments of older radiolarian chert, granophyre, possible keratophyre, and garnet probably from mica-schist. In conjunction with evidence from the Romanno Greywacke further south-west, this seems to show among other things that the volcanism which produced the soda-rich trachytes of the Tweeddale lavas was active long before the Caradoc date usually assigned to it and that the metamorphic rocks of the Highlands had reached their present petrological condition, and were already deeply exposed to erosion, in late Llandeilo time.

This is confirmed by a discovery by Mr A. Herriot and the author of albite-schist cobbles, identified by Professor Holmes, in the Llandeilo Kirkland conglomerate, near Minuntion, in the Girvan district, and by the occurrence of quartzite pebbles containing rosettes of feldspar in the Balcletchie conglomerate at Tormitchell, in the same area. The latter pebbles recall rocks described by Dr D. L. Reynolds from Colonsay, Argyllshire.

Faulting

A splay fault south of what is taken as a subsidiary fault parallel to the Southern Upland Boundary Fault in Burn C is consistent with dextral transcurrent movement. At the former dam in the same Burn, 30 ft. of basalt lava of Dalmeny type are clearly seen, from the distribution of the slaggy material, to be in a vertical position striking a little south of east-south-east. The top is to north-north-west. Only the basal $2\frac{1}{2}$ ft. of the lava is really fresh. In it, in addition to flow-aligned, fresh labradorite laths and altered microphenocrysts of olivine, there are occasional larger crystals of basic plagioclase. This lava may be compared with one in the Calciferous Sandstone Measures, $1\frac{1}{4}$ miles north-west of Noble House. The vertical position of the flow or flows proves that some of the visible fault structures at Noble House are of Carboniferous or later date. In Burn D there is an interesting roughly north-south fault which is probably Carboniferous.

The earlier history of the Southern Upland Fault at Noble House must be deduced from the types of folding in the older rocks: (1) gentle folds in grey siltstones and grits at the north end of Burn A; (2) close-packed small north-north-east plunging folds in pale green silts in Burns A, D, and E, sometimes associated with horizontal quartz veins in accompanying greywacke; (3) overthrust folds from south-south-east. These probably corresponded with three successive different types of fault movements.

Origin of Haematite-Chert

On the dating of the ferric oxide enrichment of the haematite-chert, which was among the rocks experimented with by David Mushet of Dalkeith, discoverer of the smelting value of Blackband ironstone, it can only be said that it is later than the early quartz-veining of the cherts and also later than the first red-staining of these rocks. It is prominent where thrust-planes and north-north-west faults intersect, and may have been connected with the action of hot-springs either during the Lower Old Red volcanism or during the Calciferous Sandstone volcanism represented by the Dalmeny basalt.

REFERENCES

LAMONT, A., and LINDSTRÖM, M., 1957. Arenigian and Llandeilian Cherts identified in the Southern Uplands of Scotland by means of Conodonts, etc. *Trans. Edin. Geol. Soc.* vol. 17, pp. 60–70,

MACGREGOR, M., LEE, G. W., and WILSON, G. V., 1920. *Special Reports on the Mineral Resources of Britain*, vol. 11. The Iron Ores of Scotland, pp. 213–215.

MUSHET, D., 1840. *Papers on Iron and Steel*, p. 152.

PEACH, B. N., and HORNE, J., 1899. The Silurian Rocks of Britain, vol. 1. Scotland. *Mem. Geol. Surv.* pp. 248–251, fig. 61.

RITCHIE, M., and ECKFORD, R. J. A., 1936. The 'Haggis Rock' of the Southern Uplands. *Trans. Edin. Geol. Soc.*, vol. 13, pp. 371–377,

WOOD, A., 1957. The Type-Species of the Genus *Girvanella* (Calcareous Algae). *Palæontology*, vol. 1, pp. 22–28.

A. LAMONT

DOBB'S LINN, MOFFAT

O.S. One-inch Map, Sheets 74, 79, 80, 84, 85
G.S. One-inch Map, Sheets 16, 24, 32 (Scotland)
G.S. Quarter-inch Map, Sheets 15, 17.
Locality map of Dobb's Linn, p. 146

◆

THE two routes from Edinburgh to Moffat, by Tweed or Yarrow, are roughly the same length, hence it is reasonable to make a round trip. The best views are obtained by going via the Tweed and returning over the Moorfoots. Transport by private coach or car is necessary and the itinerary involves a long day.

1. Edinburgh to Broughton: Carboniferous, Old Red Sandstone, Glacial features

Leave Edinburgh by the Penicuik road (A.701). From Penicuik, on the Upper Carboniferous of the southern part of the Midlothian Basin, continue on towards Leadburn. After climbing out of the Esk valley, the northern face of the Southern Uplands is seen ahead. Most of the slope is climbed before Leadburn which, however, is still on the Lower Carboniferous which here dips steeply to the north-west away from the Ordovician.

Three-quarters of a mile south of Leadburn, but necessitating a deviation from the direct route, the quarry in Haggis Rock near Leadburn (Craigburn Quarry, 237544) can be examined.

At Leadburn turn south-west parallel to the Southern Upland Fault and go on to the Lower Old Red Sandstone at

Romanno Bridge. Good views, to the west, of the Pentland Hills can be seen across Auchencorth Moss. The Lyne Water, crossed at Romanno Bridge, rises in the Pentlands, flows across the relatively flat beds between the Pentland and Southern Upland faults and then cuts through the Ordovician to join the River Tweed. Continue along the line of the Southern Upland Fault to Blyth Bridge and Kaimrig End. Here the Lower Old Red Sandstone conglomerates form a series of hills and the line of the fault is marked by a marshy hollow. From this point there is a broad valley running southwards to Broughton, which must be due to glacial action and which is now occupied by the small Broughton Burn.

2. Broughton to Moffat: Ordovician, Silurian, Permian

At Broughton there is the much larger and flatter valley of the Biggar Water, which has been claimed as part of the old River Tweed coming from what is now the Clyde drainage area. Continuing southwards, the Tweed is reached at Wrae where Caradocian volcanic rocks and limestone have been found. Almost immediately, however, the road passes on to Silurian greywackes with occasional bands containing Birkhill graptolites. At Tweedhopefoot the main road leaves the river and follows a tributary, then a dry valley, before rejoining the Tweed just below its source. From there the open moorland is crossed affording views of the rounded heights of Hartfell and other hills south-east of Moffat.

At a large quarry in greywacke (061126) a stop can be made to see the Devil's Beef Tub, the bottom of which is here about 500 ft. below the road. The Beef Tub is obviously partly due to glacial erosion. The whole structure cannot, however, be attributed to this cause since the floor of the hollow farther south is covered by red sandstones and conglomerate of Permian age with little evidence of faulting. Thus the hollow must be pre-Permian in part. The wooded Gallow Hill just north of Moffat consists of Silurian rocks almost surrounded

L

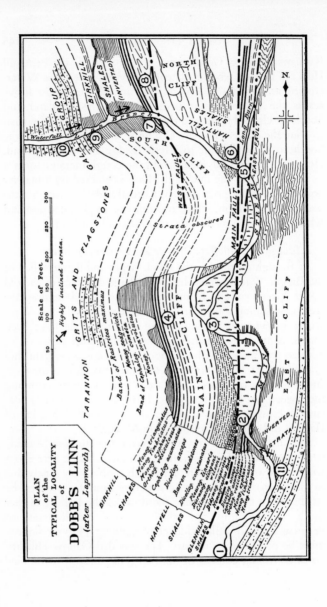

PLAN
of the
TYPICAL LOCALITY
of
DOBB'S LINN
(after Lapworth)

Scale of Feet

0 50 100 150 200 250 300

X Highly inclined strata.

TARANNON   GRITS   AND   FLAGSTONES

Band of Rastrites maximus

Monog sedgwicki

Band of Cephalog cometa

Monog convolutus

Cephalog convolutus

BIRKHILL SHALES

Monog triangulatus
Monog fimbriatus
Orthog vesiculosus

Cephalog acuminatus

Dicellog anceps

Barren Mudstones

Dicellog complanatus

Pleurog linearis
Climacog scalaris

Dicranog clingani

HARTFELL SHALES

Dicranog wilsoni
Corynoides calycularis
Glenog vesiculosus
Nemag gracilis

Monog triangulatus

GLENKILN SHALES

BIRKHILL SHALES (INVERTED)

NORTH CLIFF

HARTFELL SHALES

SOUTH CLIFF

WATERFALL

GALA GROUP

Trench

Strata obscured

WEST FAULT

MAIN FAULT

STRIKE NEAR FAULT

Long Burn

MAIN CLIFF

EAST CLIFF

INVERTED STRATA

N.

by New Red Sandstone. On the southern skyline, the flat top of Birrenswark formed by the Carboniferous volcanic rocks of the Solway basin makes a sharp contrast to the rounded Silurian hills. The road then descends gradually to Moffat.

3. Moffat to Grey Mare's Tail: Glacial and Geomorphological features

The Selkirk road out of Moffat (A.708) climbs over the shoulder from Annandale and the long, straight, flat-bottomed valley of Moffatdale stretches out ahead. It is an excellent example of a glaciated valley and owes its straightness to a fault or shatter-belt which has been traced from Moffat to St Mary's Loch and beyond by Innerleithen to the edge of the Southern Uplands near Wull Muir, a total distance of about 40 miles. The south-eastern side of the valley rises smoothly along its length to a height of 500 ft. above the floor in the lower stretch and to 1200 ft. above in the upper reaches. The north-western side has two deeply glaciated tributary valleys each with its steep sides and corrie head and with moraine at its mouth. This is well seen at Carrifran (159115) where the present small stream cuts through the corner of the moraine.

On reaching the Grey Mare's Tail, the first of the 'hanging' tributaries is seen plunging some 700 ft. from Loch Skene on the plateau above into a narrow gorge which contrasts strongly with the wide valley farther south. The Tail Burn forms about half the Moffat Water, the other half coming from three small streams which descend rapidly from the watershed near Birkhill cottage. The 350-ft. descent from the watershed to the Tail Burn takes place in $1\frac{1}{4}$ miles; the remaining 450-ft. drop to the Annan at Threewater Foot occupies $9\frac{1}{2}$ miles. By contrast the valley beyond Birkhill has a uniform gentle slope and only descends 350 ft. in the 10 miles to the Gordon Arms Inn.

4. Dobb's Linn: Silurian and Ordovician Graptolite Shales

Coaches can be left at the Grey Mare's Tail and the road followed up to Dobb's Linn but there is usually room for

parking at the bridge where the road crosses Raking Gill
(197154). Immediately below this point, the three small
streams referred to above meet and Dobb's Linn is the north-
western one of these. The name really belongs to the waterfall,
hidden from the road, which is a smaller version of the Grey
Mare's Tail. The stream plunges down the vertical Silurian
grits in a series of steps and has cut a beautiful section through
the Birkhill Shales before it joins the Long Burn and turns at
right angles to run below the Main Cliff. The rocks at Dobb's
Linn are in the form of an anticline, partially overturned and
broken by faulting, so that in general the oldest beds are exposed in the centre of the main gorge and the younger beds on
either side with the Gala Grits making the upper parts of the
cliffs. Owing to scree covering and the instability of the cliffs,
it is not possible to collect from a single complete section of
the graptolite shales. Fossils are, however, abundant on the
screes and the horizons can often be determined from the
lithology.

The sequence, as worked out by Lapworth (1878), is as
follows:

Gala Group: grits and flagstones - - -	10 ft. +
Upper Birkhill Shales: alternations of grey and black shales with many intercalated seams of white clay; zones of *Monograptus convolutus*, *M. sedgwicki* and *Rastrites maximus* - - -	77 ft.
Lower Birkhill Shales: black flaggy shales; zones of *Cephalograptus acuminatus–M. triangulatus* -	60 ft.
Upper Hartfell Shales: green, yellow and black mudstones; zones of *Dicellograptus complanatus* and *D. anceps* - - - - - -	50 ft.
Lower Hartfell Shales: black slaty shales; zones of *Climacograptus wilsoni*, *Dicranograptus clingani*, and *Pleurograptus linearis* - - -	45 ft.
Glenkiln Shales: mainly cherty black shales -	15 ft.

The southern edge of the map, (1), is about 150 yd. north of the meeting of the three streams already mentioned and about 80 yd. north of the ruined sheepfold on the west side of the stream. At the next bend of the stream (2), proceeding north, i.e. the beginning of the Main Cliff, there is a conspicuous mass of black, iron-stained shattered shales on the west side of the stream and on the slopes above, and just north of this are the only exposures of the Glenkiln Shales at this locality. Characteristic graptolites, including *Climacograptus peltifer* and *Nemagraptus*, can be obtained from the cherty shales which, however, are very well jointed and split into small cuboidal fragments. On the scree slopes above this point there are small exposures of the overlying Hartfell Shales, but good fossils are not easily obtained. If the base of the scree is followed northwards for about 50–60 yd. a good section of the upper part of the Lower Hartfell Shales is seen above the west side of the stream (3). This is in the *Pleurograptus linearis* Zone and the overlying section through the Barren Mudstones to the *Dicellograptus anceps* Zone and the succeeding basal Silurian can be worked out by scrambling up the slope. The bluffs immediately above the scree slope (4) are in the harder *Orthograptus vesiculosus* beds but collecting from this horizon and the higher zones is best done in the stream section below the waterfall or on the North Cliff.

Descend again to the stream and follow it to the junction of the Long Burn and the Linn Branch (5). On the upper slopes north of the junction there are good exposures (6) of the thin-bedded black shales of the *Dicranograptus clingani* Zone, which is poorly exposed in the Main Cliff. Large slabs covered with Orthograptids are easily obtained here and the zone fossil is occasionally found. *Climacograptus caudatus* is common.

From here there is a path along the North Cliff which provides exposures of the higher beds. If the stream is low it is easy to follow the section up the Linn Branch from the junction with the Long Burn. The first part is largely in Barren

Mudstones which are then faulted against the *O. vesiculosus* beds on the south side of the stream (7). The basal Silurian and D. *anceps* beds are seen higher up on the North Cliff (8). The higher Silurian beds can then be found in succession up to the base of the waterfall, all the beds being inverted and dipping downstream at high angles. The *Rastrites maximus* beds crop out in the sides of the pool below the first waterfall (9) but the fossiliferous bands are very thin and yield few graptolites. Some very fine large bottom structures can be seen on the grits in the main waterfall (10), about half-way up, but they are not readily attainable. More accessible exposures of the *R. maximus* Zone occur at the south end of the section shown on the map in the bed of the stream and on the east bank (11), again in inverted section with the grits dipping steeply below the shales.

5. Grey Mare's Tail to Innerleithen: Silurian

Return to the coach and proceed towards Selkirk. At Birkhill cottage, on the watershed, a plaque on the wall commemorates Lapworth's work in this area. The road now runs down a broad valley to the Loch of the Lowes and St Mary's Loch and on to the Gordon Arms Inn. Here take the north road (B.709) past Mountbenger to rejoin the line of the shatter-belt (wrench fault on G.S. Sheet 24) and over Paddock Slack to the Newhall Burn. At Cowpeel Bridge (314310), about 4 miles south of Innerleithen, where the road crosses the Newhall Burn, there is a good roadside exposure of bottom structures in the Silurian greywackes. The beds are inverted, as shown by graded bedding; they also display a variety of lower surface structures—in particular flute casts and load casts, which are illustrated by Pringle and Eckford (1945).

A diversion may be made after this to Grieston Quarry (Silurian greywackes and shales with graptolites) by taking the Peebles road (B.7062) past Traquair gates to Howford farm

(318362) and climbing up to the old tips which can be seen from the road.

6. Pirn Quarry: Silurian Sediments and Structures

Continue on to Innerliethen and take the Galashiels road for about a mile to Pirn Quarry in which Lapworth recorded graptolites, and where excellent lower surface structures may be examined (Walton 1955).

Return to the Edinburgh road and continue northward along the Leithen Water and Garvald to join the main Galashiels road near Middleton (see Middleton and Heriot excursion).

REFERENCES

LAPWORTH, C., 1878. The Moffat Series. *Quart. Jour. Geol. Soc.*, vol. 34, pp. 240–346.

PEACH, B. N. and HORNE, J., 1899. The Silurian Rocks of Britain, vol. 1, Scotland. *Mem. Geol. Surv.*

PRINGLE, J. and ECKFORD, R. J. A., 1945. Structures in Silurian Greywackes near Innerleithen, Peebles. *Trans. Edin. Geol. Soc.*, vol. 14, pp. 5–7.

RITCHIE, M. and ECKFORD, R. J. A., 1936. The 'Haggis Rock' of the Southern Uplands. *Trans. Edin. Geol. Soc.*, vol. 13, pp. 371–377.

WALTON, E. K., 1955. Silurian Greywackes in Peeblesshire. *Proc. Roy. Soc. Edin.* B., vol. 65, pp. 327–57.

ISLES STRACHAN

LEADHILLS DISTRICT

O.S. One-inch Map, Sheet 68
G.S. One-inch Map, Sheet 15 (Scotland)
Route-map p. 154

◆

THE Leadhills-Wanlockhead district is of considerable geological interest from two aspects. Firstly, it contains the largest
lead-zinc deposit that has been worked in Scotland. It also has
the longest history of production and by far the greatest out-
put of all the lead-zinc mining areas of Scotland. Secondly, the
district includes part of one of the belts of inliers of Arenig
rocks in upper Ordovician strata extending right across the
Southern Uplands.

There is no doubt that the complex structure which includes
the Arenig rocks has played a major part in localizing the ore
shoots in this area. Porteous (1876) mentions that in the Bay
Vein the miners noted that the richest part of the ore was
located 'under a bed of clay'. J. Mitchell, a former manager of
the Wanlockhead lead mines, observed that the East and West
Glencrieff Veins tended to 'cut out' in a soft black 'shale'.
During the recent period of mining activity in the district it
was possible to examine some of the underground exposures
of this material (Mackay 1959). It proved to be crush rock
showing a very marked orientation of inclusions, which were
of several different rock types. Several additional crush zones
were visible in the main drainage adit on the Leadhills side.

A close examination of the exposures of the chert-shale zone
between Laggan Gill and the Wanlock Water, together with
the long underground section in the drainage adit in the Glen-

gonnar Water Valley below Leadhills, shows that what little isoclinal folding occurs is entirely subordinate to the intense faulting and thrusting of these rocks. Unfortunately, because of the paucity of exposures between the cleughs, it seems unlikely that a detailed picture can be built up of the chert-shale zone. It may be that the chert-shale zone is a zone of imbrication with the sole thrust, passing through the Glencrieff shaft, forming one of the major ore controls in the district.

The structure of the greywackes, which lie to the south-east of the chert-shale zone, is obscure. Such evidence as can be found indicates an anticlinal structure bringing Arenig rocks to the surface in a belt from Leadburn to the Mennock Water between Lowther Hill and Middle Moor.

As public transport into the area is infrequent it is well-nigh essential to employ private conveyances. It is inadvisable to visit the district during the grouse-shooting season. Old adits should not be entered as some are extremely dangerous. Some private houses can supply teas for a few persons; excellent catering facilities are available at the Hopetoun Arms Hotel.

The best approach from Edinburgh is by way of Biggar to Abington. Thence proceed by way of road B.797 to the first exposure in the Glengonnar Water.

1. Clowgill Dod, West Face: Arenig Sediments

Clowgill Dod provides good exposures of volcanic rocks, shales and cherts showing red-staining of the cherts. The structural relationships of the rock types are difficult to assess.

Following the course of the Bellgill Burn from the last outcrops, one can examine exposures of chert and shale in the bed of the burn till the foot of a dry cleugh is reached at 893178. This cleugh gives a fine section, on the north face, of shales showing the typical bleaching effect which occurs in the shales close to outcrop in this area. Close examination shows that the shales have been considerably faulted. The south face of the section is of greywacke which has been faulted against the shales.

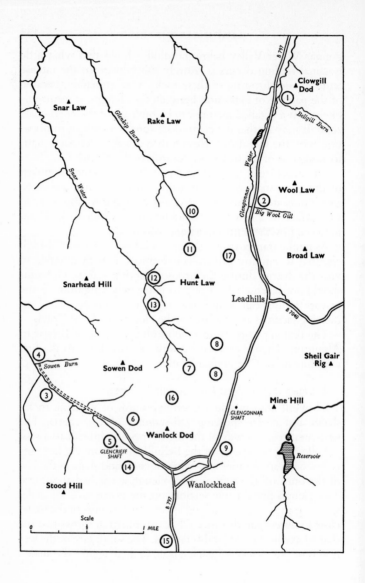

Following the burn towards its source it can be seen that there are no further outcrops of chert after the outcrop in the burn bed 50 yd. upstream from the cleugh. No outcrops of chert or shale are seen beyond point 895176 in the stream. The greywackes beyond this point are more massive with well-developed jointing. In some places sedimentation structures can be seen on water-worn surfaces. Further upstream the first of the old lead mines of Bulmer's Moss occurs.

Return to road and continue for nearly a mile towards Leadhills until Big Wool Gill is reached.

2. Big Wool Gill: Greywackes and Mine Dumps

Big Wool Gill gives an excellent section through the vein-bearing greywackes. Near the bottom of the stream in the wood (886166) exposures of a felsite dyke can be seen. A few yards to the north of this point is a mine dump round an old mine shaft. The waste material is all sheared black shale, which occurs, together with chert near one of the main crush zones in the drainage adit across the road. On the other side of the road round the old mine shaft occurs a chert outcrop (884166). This can be seen underground to be in faulted contact with the greywacke. Further up the Glengonnar Water these greywackes can be seen to crop out. The north-east to south-west face of the chert outcrop (884166) is close to the actual line of the fault which is seen underground.

3. Wanlock Water: Faulted Chert and Greywacke

From the smelt mill going south-east along Wanlock Water one or two small exposures of chert can be seen. Opposite the old crush mill at 858140 there are outcrops of shale and chert. The shaly material has been intensely crushed, intruded by quartz veinlets and silicified. Apart from the quartz veinlets and silicification the material is similar to some found along the planes of the reverse faults in this region and this outcrop is the only accessible exposure of a major fault line in the neighbourhood.

Continue a short distance to the north-west to Sowen Burn.

4. Sowen Burn: Graptolite Shale

The Sowen Burn joins Wanlock Water at 855145. On the south side of the burn the flues of the old ore smelting mill can be seen. Owing to the fumes from the smelting a large area has been denuded of all vegetation. Consequently a miniature 'Bad Lands' topography has developed. In the bottom of the narrow gullies good exposures can be seen.

Chert and black shales predominate in the exposures in the Sowen Burn. Some of the black shales near the bottom of the stream and some outcrops at the very top have yielded good graptolites. Peach and Horne (1899, p. 293) record a number of species, including *Dicranograptus ramosus*, *Glyptograptus (Diplograptus) teretiusculus var. euglyphus* and *Dicellograptus sextans*. The exposures at the top of the burn are well developed and show faulted contacts between shale and chert.

Return towards Wanlockhead until Glencrieff Shaft is reached.

5. Glencrieff Mine Dumps: Primary Minerals

A close examination of the dumps round Glencrieff Shaft should yield representative specimens of all the primary minerals which occur in the veins in this district. Good specimens of the following minerals can be found: galena, sphalerite, chalcopyrite, pyrite. Good specimens of the following gangue minerals are also easy to find: ankerite, calcite, barytes, quartz. Rare primary minerals include marcasite, niccolite, rammelsbergite, cobaltite (Temple 1956).

Leave transport at Glencrieff Shaft and walk eastwards to Whyte's Cleugh. The transport should proceed to Glengonnar Shaft to await the party.

The following localities are probably the most rewarding in secondary minerals. Digging into the dumps is unlikely to be very rewarding. A close examination of the dump edges and any disturbed areas of the dump which have been washed by rain is more profitable. Excessive collecting is to be discouraged.

Specimens of the following secondary minerals may be found in one or all of the three localities listed below; some are quite common, others rare: cerussite, anglesite, leadhillite, linarite, pyromorphite, vanadinite, smithsonite, hydrozincite, hemimorphite, malachite, azurite, chrysocolla.

6. Whyte's Cleugh: Secondary Minerals

Whyte's Cleugh is accessible by a dirt road leaving the Wanlockhead road at 867134. There is a large flat area round the Bay Shaft. The valley floor from this point is worth examination, as the whole has been filled in with the broken vein material. A large dump of material recently removed from the Whyte's Cleugh adit is very rewarding in secondary minerals. The Cove Vein dumps may occasionally give good results if fresh exposures are available.

Follow a rather poorly defined footpath from Whyte's Cleugh to the dumps at the head of Snar Water.

7. Dumps at Head of Snar Water: Secondary Minerals

The dumps at the head of Snar Water can be particularly fruitful. Linarite is occasionally found in the cores of weathered nodules. Close examination is worthwhile as many of the specimens are quite small.

Continue thence to Hopeful Vein, Sarrowcole Vein Dumps.

8. Hopeful Vein—Sarrowcole Vein Dumps: Secondary Minerals

Vein dumps extend northwards from the Lady Ann Hopetoun Shaft at 880142. There are many small shafts in this area and, possibly, a little opencast work took place.

Pyromorphite is quite common as small crystals on gangue material. This is the area in which Temple (1956) made most of his discoveries. Further north at the junction of the Sarrow-cole, Laverockhall veins and George's Roust vein there are a number of small shafts and possibly some opencasts. These again contain pyromorphite and other secondary minerals, all as small specimens.

Return to the main road north of Wanlockhead and make for the old railway cutting.

9. Railway Cutting, Wanlockhead: Outcrops of Veins

The railway cutting between Wanlockhead and the Glengonnar Shaft, 879131 to 881136, passes through greywacke in which can be seen the outcrops of several veins. These include Lee's, West Stayvoyage, East Stayvoyage and possibly one or two lesser veins. The actual veins are marked by limonite and hæmatite staining along fault planes.

Return to Glengonnar Shaft and rejoin transport for return journey.

The excursion described will occupy a full day in the field. For those who may wish to spend more time in the district the additional localities 10 to 17 will afford further opportunities for the study of chert-shale relationships and the collection of minerals.

10. Scar to the north of Glenkip Head: Faulted Greywacke and Chert

An excellent exposure of a faulted junction between greywacke and chert occurs in the scar which joins the Glenkip Burn (876164). The north face of the scar is composed of greywacke nearly to the top where there are narrow outcrops of shale and chert. The south face of the scar is entirely chert except for a small outcrop of black shales at the very bottom of the scar.

11. Glenkiphead: Chert, Shale and Greywacke

A series of exposures of chert, shales and greywackes occurs at Glenkiphead but no volcanic rocks have been noted in these exposures. The most northern of this group of scars is in typical black shales which have been bleached. Some poorly preserved graptolites have been found in this outcrop. The other scars contain outcrops of the three main rock types. The outcrops are sporadic and contacts are rare.

The only known example in the district of a naturally occurring gossan appears in this area.

The outcrops are in the line of strike of the next group of outcrops (12).

12. The Hunt Law Scar: Chert, Shale and Greywacke

The more northerly scar joins the Snar Water at 870156. This scar has a complex series of outcrops of chert, shale and greywacke over a vertical range of 300 ft. in 300 yd. The southern scar (871154) has a similar series of outcrops in approximately the same height range. These two scars show very clearly the complexity of the chert–shale zone in the vertical direction.

There is one small outcrop of volcanic rock at the edge of the dressing floor near the bottom of the southern scar. This is structurally the lowest outcrop of the volcanic rocks that has been seen in the district.

13. Lamb Knowes Area: Sediments and Dumps with Mineralization

In the area of the stream junction (870155) the chert-shale outcrops are a continuation of the Hunt Law scar outcrops. In the western branch of the stream greywacke occurs from 869153 to beyond a group of small mines on the east bank of the stream. Samples of vein material from the dumps round these mines show post-mineralization brecciation. Black shales and chert occur again in the stream just before the junction with the Sowen Dod tributary. This tributary also has out-crops of chert and shale for a short distance but greywacke outcrops all the rest of the way to Sowen Dod.

All the small tributaries of the Snar Water, as they are traced towards their sources on Wanlock Dod and Laverock Hall have outcrops of chert and shale. The most interesting outcrop is along the stream and the steep banking from 874149 to 876148 showing black shales occurring under greywacke.

14. Glencrieff: Mineralized Greywacke

A steep little valley joins the Wanlock Water at 868132. The outcrops are all in greywacke typical of the mineralized area. Immediately above the entrance to the Glencrieff Horse Level at 867128 there is a waterfall. The rock which forms the waterfall is apparently greywacke on megascopic examination. Microscopic examination reveals that most of the greywacke has been replaced by dolomite. The dolomite occurs as euhedral or subhedral crystals. This dolomitized greywacke has been noted in only one other place, underground in a cross-cut from the drainage adit from the Lochnell vein. The cause and associations of the dolomitization are unknown.

15. Corbie Linn: Graded Bedding and Conglomeratic Greywacke

A narrow gully accessible from a dirt road at 873121 is in typical greywacke. Some examples of graded bedding can be found in the fragments in the talus at the bottom of the gully. At the top a smaller gully extends north from the main gully. In the east face there is a small outcrop of a very well developed conglomeratic greywacke with sharp unworn rock fragments. A number of rock types can easily be distinguished.

16. Belton Grain Vein Dumps: Minerals Including Vanadinite

Dumps extend from 873141 to 874137 and probably include the High Pirn Mine which is a locality for vanadinite. All these dumps are very old and the surfaces are much weathered.

Close examination is worthwhile. The dumps are accessible by footpaths either from Whyte's Cleugh or Leadhills.

17. Lady Manner's Scar: Opencast Workings

Opencast workings on the Susanna Vein on Lady Manner's Scar is the type locality for a number of minerals but is not now so fruitful as locations 6, 7 and 8. Small specimens of jamesonite have been found as veinlets in some fragments of dump material.

REFERENCES

BROWN, R., 1919. The mines and Minerals of Leadhills. *Trans. Dumfr. & Gall. Nat. Hist. Soc.*, vol. 6, p. 24.

———., 1925. More about the mines and minerals of Wanlockhead and Leadhills. *Trans. Dumfr. & Gall. Nat. Hist. Soc.*, vol. 13, p. 58.

MACKAY, R. A., 1959. The Leadhills Wanlockhead Mining District. Symposium on The future of Non-ferrous Mining in Great Britain and Ireland. *The Institution of Mining and Metallurgy.*

PEACH, B. N. and HORNE, J., 1899. The Silurian Rocks of Britain, vol. 1 Scotland *Mem. Geol. Surv.*

PORTEOUS, J. M., 1876. *God's Treasure-house in Scotland.* A history of times, mines and lands in the Southern Highlands. London.

TEMPLE, A. K., 1956. The Leadhills-Wanlockhead Lead and Zinc Deposits. *Trans. Roy. Soc. Edin.*, vol. 63, p. 85.

WILSON, G. V., 1921. The Lead, Zinc, Copper and Nickel ores of Scotland. *Spec. Rep. Miner, Resour.* 17. *Geol. Surv.*

Mackay (1959) gives an excellent background for all aspects of the geology of this district.

G. W. BORTHWICK

THE NORTH ESK INLIER

O.S. One-inch Map, Seventh Series, Sheet 62
G.S. One-inch Map, Sheet 32 (Scotland)
Route-map p. 166

◆

ACCESS is by public bus (Scottish Omnibuses Ltd.) to Carlops and then by footpath along north bank of River Esk towards North Esk Reservoir. Private cars and buses may be taken along the rough road from Carlops as far as the waterman's cottage at the North Esk Reservoir. As described, the itinerary will occupy a long day and may well be found to occupy more than one day, especially if much time is spent in collecting.

The North Esk—Lyne Water inlier is the largest and most important of the three Silurian inliers in the Pentland Hills. It is composed of highly inclined or vertical strata which strike in a south-westerly direction and, as a rule, younger beds come in to the north-west. The Silurian beds are overlain by the Lower Old Red Sandstone greywacke-conglomerate which rests with a marked angular unconformity on their truncated edges.

It has long been thought that the age of the Silurian rocks in the Pentland Hills ranges from Wenlock to Downtonian. A detailed re-investigation of the Pentland fauna by Dr A. Lamont has, however, suggested that the beds formerly classed as Wenlock and Ludlow belong to the formation lying between the Upper Llandovery and basal Wenlock, and fall largely within the zone of *Monoclimacis crenulata*. They are thus correlated with the Gala group of the Southern Uplands and the Tarannon group of the Silurian of Central Wales; Lamont has proposed the new term *Pentlandian* for this division of the Silurian System. The fauna of the beds which were formerly taken as Downton is now tentatively assigned to the Wenlock.

The fossiliferous strata of the North Esk inlier were intensely studied during the last century by several local geologists, and John Henderson and D. J. Brown were able to recognize eight distinct palæontological zones (A to H) in the fossiliferous beds exposed in the River North Esk and its tributaries. The discovery of thin beds with Eurypterids and Starfish in the Gutterford Burn by Henderson led to intensive collecting from these beds by Mr Hardie of Bavelaw. The Hardie collection is now lodged with the Royal Scottish Museum in Edinburgh.

The following table gives the succession of the Silurian strata in the inlier; the approximate thicknesses of the various divisions can be roughly estimated from the map (p. 166) if it is assumed that the beds are near vertical throughout, and that repetition by folding is insignificant:

B. *Formerly included in Downton, now tentatively assigned to Wenlock:*

	Locality on map
10. Red sandstone with bands of pebbly grit near top	25
9. Red and greenish mudstones and siltstones with thick greywacke posts near top. Lynslie Burn fish-bed with *Birkenia*, *Ateleaspis* and *Lasanius* near base.	24
8. Red sandstone with lenses of pebbly grit and conglomerate.	26
7. Olive-green shales and siltstones with some greywacke ribs. Includes Lyne Water fish-bed with *Ateleaspis*, *Spirorbis* and plants. (Not exposed in North Esk and Henshaw Burn.)	27

6. Red sandstone with lens of quartzite conglomerate near top. (Conglomerate found only in Henshaw Burn.) Lenses of pebbly grit with igneous
pebbles throughout.   21, 28

5. Red conglomerate with igneous pebbles including acid lavas and alkali-granite.   20, 22, 29

A. *Formerly taken as Ludlow and Wenlock, now assigned to Gala-
Tarannon (Pentlandian):*

*Locality
on map*

4. Marine mudstones and siltstones with abundant
fossils, comprising beds D to H of Henderson and
Brown:

Bed H: Bluish-green and dark brown mudstones and siltstones with abundant '*Euomphalopterus*' *simulans*, '*Rhynchonella*' *pentlandica*
and *Slimonia*.   19, 22, 30

Bed G: Sandy siltstone, yellowish-brown,
spheroidal weathering, sparsely fossiliferous.   18

Bed F: Greenish-brown sandstones and silt-
stones with abundant '*Orthoceras maclareni*'.   16, 17

Bed E: Greenish-grey mudstones and shales with
sandy bands; highly fossiliferous with abundant *Plectodonta* aff. *canastonensis*. The '*Plectodonta* mudstones' of Lamont form the lower
part of this division.   13, 14

Bed D: Greenish-grey shales and sandy beds,
highly fossiliferous (no longer well exposed
in River North Esk).   13

3. Hard sandstones and quartzose grits with bands
of pebbly grit containing small round pebbles of
quartzite and igneous rock. (Bed C of Henderson
and Brown; 'Haggis' grit and conglomerate of
Lamont.) Occasional fossils.   12

2. Green and purplish-grey flagstones with thin

bands of shale and a thin band of fossiliferous siltstone.

NOTE: These beds are tentatively correlated by Lamont with the 'Gutterford Flags' which contain the *Starfish Beds* (Locs. 8 and 9), the *Eurypterid Bed* (Loc. 6) and the *Gutterford Burn Limestone* (Loc. 5), and which have yielded occasional graptolites including *Monograptus priodon, Monoclimacis crenulata, Coremagraptus, Acanthograptus, Dictyonema venustum and Dictyonema (Chondrites) verisimile.*   4, 5, 6, 7, 8, 9

1. Purple and grey mudstones and siltstones, flaggy greywacke ribs towards base, fossils scarce.   1, 2, 3, 10

From Carlops the path along the North Esk passes over conglomerate and grit of Lower Old Red Sandstone age, which is well exposed in rock ledges in the stream just above Carlops Mill. Some 60 yd. west of the mill, exposures of shattered pyroxene-andesite, which belong to the Carnethy group of the Pentland Hills, are seen by the side of the path. From there the North Esk traverses the complete sequence of the basal Old Red Sandstone pebbly grits and greywacke conglomerates from the lowest lava flow to the post-Silurian unconformity.

Several of the sub-basic minor intrusions of Old Red Sandstone age are easily accessible from the path. An intrusion consisting of three connected sills is exposed in the rocky outcrop between the path and the stream 160 yd. below its junction with the Fairliehope Burn. Other sills are well exposed on the banks of the North Esk above its junction with this burn, in the Fairliehope Burn itself about 60 yd. above the stream-junction, and in a small quarry on the roadside 70 yd. west-north-west of Fairliehope Farm. Cockburn has suggested that these various outcrops represent exposures of a single somewhat transgressive and branching sill.

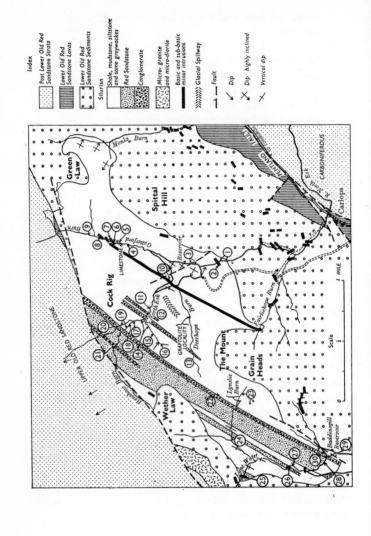

Index

Post Lower Old Red Sandstone Strata

Lower Old Red Sandstone Lavas

Lower Old Red Sandstone Sediments

Silurian
Shale, mudstone, siltstone and some greywackes

Red Sandstone

Conglomerate

Micro-granite and micro-diorite

Basic and sub-basic minor intrusions

Glacial Spillway

Fault

Dip

Dip - highly inclined

Vertical dip

1, 2 and 3. South of North Esk Reservoir: Old Red Sandstone—Silurian junction

The plane of unconformity between Silurian and Old Red Sandstone is not exposed, but its position can be closely located on the banks of the stream 420 yd. south-east of the reservoir (1). The Silurian strata below the unconformity are grey, greenish and reddish mudstones and siltstones with occasional grit bands. Close to the unconformity the strike of the Silurian is almost at right angles to the regional strike and the beds are somewhat contorted. This contortion may be due to hill-creep below the pre-Lower Old Red Sandstone land surface. Fossils are rare.

The gorge (2) cut by the overflow waters from the North Esk Reservoir provides an excellent section in a sequence of purple and grey shales and mudstones, with flaggy greywacke ribs in a part of the section. The strike of these beds is mainly north-north-east to north-east in accordance with the regional strike, but the presence of a recumbent eastward-closing fold with a near horizontal axis, as is seen in the deepest part of the gorge, is a feature found nowhere else in the inlier. Small-scale current-bedding in some of the greywacke ribs indicates that the beds 'young' to the north-west. It has, indeed, been recorded by Lamont that 'younging' to the north-west is the general rule in the Pentland succession.

At low water an excellent section is exposed on the east bank of the North Esk Reservoir (3). The greywackes and siltstones near the south-east corner of the reservoir yield abundant fragments of the Phyllocarid *Dictyocaris ramsayi*. About 120 yd. north of the south-east corner, the beds are highly crushed, though slickensiding is not very prominent. Dr Lamont has suggested that this crushed zone marks the line of a great west-north-west crush belt.

4–9. Gutterford Burn: Starfish and Eurypterid Beds

The purple and grey mudstones exposed in the lower part

of the Gutterford Burn (4) are overlain by grey siltstones and mudstones with thin ribs of greywacke. These beds, like the underlying mudstones, carry a very sparse shelly fauna, but they have also yielded a large proportion of the scarce graptolite fauna collected in the Pentland Hills. (See p. 165 for fossils.)

A thin limestone, up to 10 in. thick, which occurs in a succession of mudstones, siltstones and greywackes, crops out in the stream-bed and on the east bank at this locality (5). The outcrop is not easy to find as there is an absence of landmarks in the vicinity; it is 300 yd. north of the mouth of the third easterly tributary of the Gutterford Burn encountered upstream from the North Esk Reservoir. The limestone is composed largely of crinoid stems and contains corals, brachiopods and ostracods.

The Eurypterus beds, which have yielded a number of interesting species of arthropods, crop out in the river cliff on the east bank of the stream 320 yd. upstream from the third tributary mentioned above (6). They occur as very thin bands in a succession of interbedded flaggy greywackes and siltstones. A characteristic feature of these beds is the abundance of the fossil *Dictyocaris ramsayi*, which forms large black patches on the bedding planes. The Gutterford Eurypterids which, according to Dr Lamont, possess more primitive features than other well-known Eurypterid faunas found in Silurian strata elsewhere, have been described in various papers by M. Laurie.

Three small dykes, belonging to the Lower Old Red Sandstone suite of minor intrusions, are exposed on the east bank of the stream (7). They are probably branches of the thick dyke which extends from Fairliehope Burn by the North Esk Reservoir to this locality.

The 'Starfish Bed' has been recorded from two localities: on the west bank of the stream 120 yd. south of where it is crossed by a wall (8), and on the east bank 25 to 30 yd. north of the wall (9). The starfishes, including *Palæaster*, *Palasterina* and

Protaster, usually occur in thin sandy bands varying from a fraction of an inch to several inches in thickness.

10. N. Shore of N. Esk Reservoir: Dyke and Silurian Sediments

Before returning to the River North Esk, it is worth examining the fine section on the north shore of the North Esk Reservoir (10), if the water is sufficiently low. Note here especially the zone of crushed, but not greatly slickensided, beds, occurring near the middle of the shore section which may be on the line of the crush belt already noted on the east bank of the reservoir. Note also the outcrop of the Fairliehope-Gutterford dyke, which crosses the reservoir near its north-west corner.

11 and 12. Lower Part of River N. Esk: Silurian Strata

The sequence on the north bank of the reservoir and in the lower part of the North Esk above the reservoir is predominantly argillaceous and silty. These strata pass north-westwards into a sequence of greywackes with interbedded siltstones and purple shales. A layer of coarse greenish siltstone has yielded to Lamont nine new species of lamellibranchs together with Chonetids, trilobites, and some large corals (11). This band is also known in a small southern tributary of the Deerhope Burn and Lamont has suggested that it may occupy the horizon of the Gutterford Burn Limestone.

Two layers of pebbly grit with small rounded pebbles of quartzite and acid igneous rock interbedded with quartzose grits are exposed in rock knobs north of the stream and in an old quarry some 20 yd. south of the stream (12). Current-bedding seen in the grit indicates that the beds here young to the north-west. Where the pebbly grit is again exposed in the Deerhope Burn, half a mile to the south-west, it is much finer and its thickness is reduced. This seems to suggest that the source of sediments was from a north-easterly direction. In the quarry certain bands of grit and one band of shale have yielded a small collection of fossils.

13. Deerhope Burn: Middle Portion of Silurian Succession

The lowest zone of the highly fossiliferous sequence which overlies the grits (Bed D of Henderson and Brown) is best exposed on the north bank of the Deerhope Burn, some 1100 yd. west of its mouth (13). Here the grits are overlain by about 20 ft. of purple and grey sandstone, and these in turn by grey silty mudstone. A very large fauna has been collected from both bands.

14–16. Wetherlaw Linn: Middle Portion of Silurian Succession

The Wetherlaw Linn, a small tributary of the River North Esk, provides excellent exposures of Beds E and F of Henderson and Brown (14, 15). The '*Plectodonta* mudstones' of Lamont (lower part of Bed E) are well exposed on the south bank of the stream, 140 yd. west-south-west of its junction with the North Esk, where they are characterized by the abundance of *Plectodonta* aff. *canastonensis* and *Amphispongia oblonga*. They are also seen on the north bank of the Deerhope Burn 1150 yd. west-south-west of its mouth.

Bed F, which consists of greenish-brown concretionary siltstones and sandstones with *Orthoceras maclareni* as the characteristic fossil, is exposed in the upper part of the Wetherlaw Linn (16).

17–21. Higher reaches of River North Esk and Henshaw Burn: Upper Part of Silurian Succession

Bed F is also found in the North Esk just below its junction with the Henshaw Burn (17). Bed G is exposed on the east bank of the Henshaw Burn, some 20 yd. upstream from its confluence with the North Esk (18). The strata here are composed of concretionary weathering, sparsely fossiliferous, sandy siltstone. The succeeding strata (Bed H) are dark shales and siltstones which yield a large fossil assemblage characterized by the abundance of '*Euomphalopterus*' *simulans* and '*Rhynchonella*' *pentlandica*. There are a number of exposures on the west bank of the Henshaw Burn and one in the North Esk (19).

The red conglomerate and pebbly grit which was formerly taken as the base of the Downtonian is exposed on both banks of the North Esk, 230 yd. above its junction with the Henshaw Burn (20). The pebbles include alkali-granites, fine-grained silicified thyolites and andesites as well as sandstones and siltstones. The junction with the underlying grey fossiliferous strata is not exposed in this locality. Farther upstream there are occasional exposures of the red sandstone, sometimes with red mudstone pellets, which overlies the conglomeratic beds.

The red sandstones are exposed at intervals in the Henshaw Burn (21). About 450 yd. above its junction with the North Esk these contain a thin conglomerate with well-rounded pebbles of quartzite, which overlies 3 ft. 4 in. of red silty mudstone. It has been suggested in the past that this conglomerate might represent the quartzite-conglomerate which overlies the so-called 'Downtonian' fish-bed in the Lesmahagow Inlier.

The excursion can suitably be concluded at this point, and a return can be made to Carlops or by the Bore Stane (see p. 175) to Balerno. Alternatively, if the Lyne Water sequence is to be included in the itinerary, the best way is to go up the Deerhope Burn and through the small overflow channel which cuts the saddle between Wether Law and The Mount into the basin of the Lyne Water.

22. Lynslie Burn: Upper Part of Silurian Succession

A newly-cut tributary channel (22) of the Lynslie Burn provides an excellent exposure of the junction between the highest fossiliferous strata of Bed H and the overlying red grits and conglomerates.

In the headwaters of the Lynslie Burn (23), and in a small stream-cutting to the south, there are exposures of strata belonging to most of the fossiliferous zones E to H. In the eastward-flowing portion of the Lynslie Burn the strata over-lying the lowest red 'Downtonian' sandstone are exposed. In the south bank, 50 yd. east of the stream-junction (24) the red and green shales and siltstones which overlie the narrow second band of red pebbly sandstone have yielded small fragments of the fishes *Birkenia*, *Ateleaspis* and *Lasanius*, together with *Spirorbis*, crinoid stems and a sponge. These fossils are, how-ever, very rare.

25. Upper Part of Lyne Water: Highest Silurian Strata

The strata exposed in the Lyne Water above its confluence with the Lynslie Burn (25) consist of an upward sequence of unfossiliferous grey and green mudstones and siltstones, flaggy greywacke posts with shale and siltstone partings, and red sandstone with bands of pebbly grit near the top. The evidence from current-bedding and sun-cracks suggests that the whole of this sequence youngs to the north-west. If the Lyne Water is followed up for a further 300 yd. from the Silurian—Old Red Sandstone unconformity, exposures of the Lyne Water microdiorite intrusion and its south-eastern margin can be seen.

26, 27. Lower Part of Lyne Water: Upper Part of Silurian Succession

The Lyne Water below its junction with the Lynslie Burn (26) provides a repetition and amplification of the sequence seen in the Lynslie Burn. Of special interest is the Lyne Water fish-bed (27), which occurs below the second red sandstone in a brown sandy shale on the east bank of the stream, 20 yd. north of a sheepfold. This band has yielded *Glauconome* (?), *Spirorbis* and a fragment of *Ateleaspis*. Again, these fossils are very rare.

28–30. Baddinsgill Reservoir: Upper part of Silurian Succession

The lowest red sandstone, together with the underlying pebbly grit and conglomerate, is well exposed on the north bank of the Baddinsgill Reservoir. At the mouth of a small tributary stream (30) the underlying bluish-green silty mudstones with abundant '*Euomphalopterus*' *simulans* (Bed H) are again seen. In this locality the Lower Old Red Sandstone greywacke conglomerate, exposed on the east bank of the stream and reservoir, is faulted against the Silurian, and the plane of unconformity is not seen.

The return journey may be made by road to West Linton but, if time permits, it is strongly recommended that the Windy Gowl, one of the finest and most complex systems of marginal channels in Midlothian, should be followed from its intake three-quarters of a mile east of Wakefield to Carlops.

REFERENCES

COCKBURN, A. M., 1952. Minor Intrusions of the Pentland Hills. *Trans. Edin. Geol. Soc.*, vol. 15, pp. 84–99.

HENDERSON, J., and BROWN, D. J., 1867. The Silurian Rocks of the Pentland Hills. *Trans. Edin. Geol. Soc.*, vol. 1, pp. 23–33; and pp. 266–272.

LAMONT, A., 1947. Gala-Tarannon Beds in the Pentland Hills, near Edinburgh. *Geol. Mag.*, vol. 84, No. 4, pp. 193–208, No. 5, pp. 289–303.

LAMONT, A., 1952. Ecology and Correlation of the Pentlandian—A New Division of the Silurian System in Scotland. *Rept. 18th Int. Geol. Congr.*, London, Part 10, pp. 27–32.

LAMONT, A., 1954. New Lamellibranchs from the Gutterford Burn Flagstones (Gala-Tarannon) of the Pentland Hills, near Edinburgh. *Proc. Roy. Soc. Edin.*, B, vol. 65, Part III, pp. 271–284.

LAURIE, M., 1892. Some Eurypterid Remains from the Upper Silurian Rocks in the Pentland Hills. *Trans. Roy. Soc. Edin.*, vol. 37, pp. 151–161.

MACGREGOR, M., and MACGREGOR, A. G., 1948. The Midland Valley of Scotland. 2nd. edit., *British Regional Geology, Geol. Surv.*, pp. 14–15.

PEACH, B. N., and HORNE, J., 1899. The Silurian Rocks of Britain: vol. 1, Scotland. *Mem. Geol. Surv.*, pp. 589–606.

PEACH, B. N. *et al.*, 1910. The Geology of the Neighbourhood of Edinburgh. 2nd Edit., *Mem. Geol. Surv.*, pp. 10–22.

SPENCER, W. K., 1914–40. British Palæozoic Asterozoa, Parts 1–10, *Mon. Palæont. Soc.*

W. MYKURA

THE PENTLAND HILLS

O.S. One-inch Map, Seventh Series, Sheet 62
G.S. One-inch Map, Sheet 32 (Scotland)
Route-maps, pp. 176, 184

◆

THE Pentland Hills are made up of Lower Old Red Sandstone lavas and sediments with a core of Silurian rocks. The latter are generally steeply dipping and are exposed in three distinct inliers known as the North Esk, Bavelaw Castle and Loganlee-Craigenterrie inliers. The Lower Old Red Sandstone lavas consists of ten distinct groups of lava flows (Mykura, 1960, p. 134), which include olivine-basalts, andesites, trachytes, dacites and rhyolites, as well as acid and basic tuffs. They attain a thickness of over 6000 ft. in the north, but thin rapidly to the south. Near the southern end of their outcrop up to 2000 ft. of Lower Old Red Sandstone conglomerate and grit are present between the lavas and the underlying Silurian strata. Upper Old Red Sandstone, composed mainly of pink sandstone, rests unconformably on an eroded and undulating land surface of the older rocks. It forms the East and West Cairn Hills in the south-western part of the range, but near the northern end of the Pentlands, at Torphin Hill, it is very thin and in places completely overlapped by basal Carboniferous beds.

The present topographic pattern of the Pentland Hills was initiated in the Tertiary era, and was later modified by the Highland ice which overwhelmed the area in Pleistocene times. Thus some of the Pentland passes, such as the Cauld Stane Slap and the Bore Stane, are sited on the beheaded

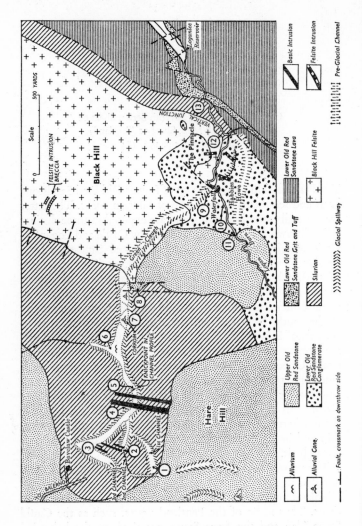

North slope of Hare Hill, Pentland Hills
Marginal Glacial Drainage Channel

courses of Tertiary rivers which drained to the south-east, while other major through-routes were formed as late-glacial overflow channels carrying melt-waters from ice-dammed lakes on the north-west slopes of the range into the Midlothian Basin.

The itinerary forms the basis for two half-day excursions from Edinburgh. Alternatively, the two sections may be combined to make one very long day-excursion.

EXCURSION A

Bavelaw Castle to Loganlee Reservoir (Route-map p. 176)

Access is by public bus (S.M.T.) to Balerno and then $2\frac{1}{2}$ miles walking distance to Bavelaw Castle. The return journey can be made by walking via Glencorse Reservoir to Flotterstone and thence by S.M.T. bus to Edinburgh.

The route from Bavelaw Castle to Flotterstone follows one of the major glacial spillways in the Pentland Hills.

1. Bavelaw Castle: Marginal Glacial Channels

A traverse from the road-end at Bavelaw Castle to the wall on the north-west slope of Hare Hill, 640 yd. to the south, crosses the intakes of three successive marginal channels which carried melt-waters from an ice-dammed lake just west of Hare Hill via Green Cleugh to Loganlee. The courses of the two higher channels are successively truncated by those of the lower ones, and east of a point 450 yd. south-east of Bavelaw Castle the course of the highest channel was used and deepened during the two later ice-retreat stages.

Locality 1 forms a good viewpoint from which the following features can be observed:

(a) Two small horseshoe-shaped marginal channels in low ground immediately to the south which were used successively to drain melt-waters first to the north and then to the south.

(b) The profile of the north slope of Hare Hill, originally an

N

evenly sloping hillside in which the Bavelaw-Loganlee marginal channel is now entrenched.

(c) The alluvial flat extending for three-quarters of a mile west-south-westward from Threipmuir Reservoir, which was part of the floor of an ice-dammed lake formed at a later stage in the retreat of the ice-sheet. The waters from this lake escaped through the gap between Black Hill and Bell's Hill to join the lower part of the Bavelaw-Loganlee channel which flowed by Glencorse Reservoir to Flotterstone.

(d) The flat top of East Cairn Hill (1839 ft.), which is thought to be a residual portion of the Tertiary 2000-ft. peneplane.

Other features of interest easily seen from here are (left to right): Corston Hill, composed of mugearite and olivine-basalt lavas of basal Oil-Shale Group (Arthur's Seat Volcanics) age; Dalmahoy Hill, a sill of teschenitic dolerite containing the rare mineral chlorophæite; and Ratho Hill, a sill of quartz-dolerite.

2 and 3. Bavelaw Castle: Silurian

Silurian rocks of the Bavelaw Castle inlier are exposed in two small quarries south and west of Bavelaw Castle (2, 3). The strata are nearly vertical and consist of grey-green mudstones with silty laminæ. They are rather poorly fossiliferous and some of the genera recorded are *Glassia*, *Lingula*, *Phacops*, *Euomphalus*, *Pleurotomaria*, *Theca*, *Orthoceras* and *Ctenodonta*.

The beds of the Bavelaw Castle inlier have long been thought to be of Wenlock age, but recently Dr A. Lamont has shown that they are of Gala-Tarannon age and belong to the oldest Silurian rocks exposed in the Pentland Hills. In both the quarries the sediments are intruded by dykes of fine-grained andesine-dolerite. There are five dykes varying in thickness from 3 ft. to 11 ft. 6 in. in the northern quarry and two, respectively 3 to 4 ft. and 25 ft. thick, in the southern; most of the dykes are slightly transgressive.

4. North of Hare Hill: Dykes

A large dyke-swarm of highly decomposed basic rocks is exposed on the slopes of the marginal channel between 540 and 600 yd. south-east of Bavelaw Castle (4). The most westerly of these dykes may be up to 150 ft. thick and all are so highly decomposed that they are easily mistaken for grit.

5 and 6. North of Hare Hill: Glacial Drainage Channels

The valley profile of the channel is evenly graded as far as a point 630 yd. south-east of Bavelaw Castle (5). Beyond this point the gradient steepens slightly and the valley floor loses some of the characteristic flatness of a marginal channel.

Eight hundred yards east-south-east of Bavelaw Castle (6), the north bank of the original east-west channel is breached and a secondary channel leads off northwards. This branch-channel has the shape of a typical spillway for the first 150 yd. of its course, but beyond this it deteriorates into a normal stream valley. The explanation for this branch-channel appears to be that, as the height of the north bank of the present through-channel is very low at this point, the north bank of the melt-water channel during its active life was here almost entirely formed by the southern front of the ice-sheet. When the ice-sheet eventually retreated, some of the melt-water was able to escape northwards, and cut a short north-south rock-channel before spilling on to the ice. Eventually, as the amount of melt-water passing through the main channel decreased, the entire drainage would pass through this northern outlet. This led to a local steepening of the gradient in the original through-channel west of this outlet, and a complete reversal of gradient for a short distance east of it, the limit of back-cutting in both cases being marked by knick-points. About 200 to 400 yd. farther south-east, two small streamlets, which have cut gullies into the north slope of Hare Hill, have deposited small alluvial cones on the flat bottom of the main spillway. The westerly of these cones now forms the water-shed in the channel and is thus an example of a delta-watershed or corrom.

7 and 8. North-east of Hare Hill: Silurian, Old Red Sandstone and Felsite

The westerly of the two gullies (7) cut in the south bank of the channel exposes fossiliferous Silurian strata, which consist of purplish-grey siltstones and mudstones with thin ochre-coloured flaggy ribs. The fossils recorded in this locality include *Monograptus*, *Retiolites*, *Dictyocaris*, *Lingula* and *Orthoceras*.

The western bank of the second gully (8) shows Silurian strata which dip steeply to the west-south-west and have yielded *Acidaspis*, *Glassia*, *Meristella*, *Cucullela*, *Theca* and *Orthoceras*. The east bank of the gully is cut in Upper Old Red Sandstone, which consists of pink sandstone with layers full of sub-angular pebbles of quartzite and Pentland lavas; this has been faulted down against the Silurian to the west. There is some evidence for the presence of small westward-hading reversed faults in this area, and it is possible that the Silurian is here thrust over the Upper Old Red Sandstone. For a short distance east of the gully, Upper Old Red Sandstone rests directly on Silurian, but about 30 yd. east of the small sandstone cliff an exposure in a small water-scoop shows Upper Old Red Sandstone resting on weathered felsite.

Felsite is exposed for some distance on both sides of Green Cleugh, and the accumulation of its platy scree has here largely obliterated the original cross-section of the glacial spillway. The felsite which forms the whole of Black Hill has in thin section the characteristics of microgranite, and is a very distinctive rock as it contains many porphyritic crystals of micropegmatite (a graphic intergrowth of quartz and feldspar). Near Habbies Howe the felsite on the slope of Black Hill is overlain by a thin cap of Lower Old Red Sandstone conglomerate, which dips 'off' Black Hill at 20°–25° to the south-south-west.

9–11. Logan Water: Lower Old Red Sandstone Conglomerate, Glacial features

Lower Old Red Sandstone conglomerate is well exposed in the gorge of the Logan Water between localities 9 and 11. It is a typical fluvial conglomerate with abundant well-rounded pebbles of greywacke, jasperised basic lava and radiolarian chert, which were probably derived from the south. Blocks of Silurian limestone, which have yielded the corals *Tetradium, Favosites, Halysites, Plasmopora, Heliolites* and other fossils, including trilobites, brachiopods and orthocones, are found 100 to 150 yd. upstream from the lowest waterfall (10). Near the base of the section the conglomerate passes down into a brownish pebbly grit which contains, in addition to the rounded pebbles mentioned above, some smaller angular pebbles of igneous rocks. The latter are largely trachytes and more basic lavas, but a number are composed of felsite containing phenocrysts of micropegmatite identical to those found in the Black Hill felsite. Such felsite fragments are well seen in some loose blocks of conglomerate lying just east of the stream at the point where it emerges from its gorge on to the flat bottom of the glacial channel. The conglomerate, both in the gorge and in the cliff to the east, is cut by irregular sills and dykes of Black Hill felsite and there is also a sill of andesine-dolerite which crosses the lowest waterfall.

There is a marked change in the character of the valley of the Logan Burn at a point 270 yd. upstream from the waterfall (11). Above this, the stream flows in a fairly wide valley which is largely floored by boulder clay; below, it passes into an ungraded post-glacial rock gorge. The pre-glacial course of the Logan Burn runs to the south of Habbies Howe cliff and joins the present course of the stream about 450 yd. south-west of Loganlee.

12. South-west of Loganlee Reservoir: Black Hill Felsite and Silurian

The vertical junction of the Black Hill felsite, with the Silurian strata of the Loganlee-Craigenterrie inlier, is exposed just north of the path 500 yd. south-west of Loganlee Reservoir. Slightly higher up the hillside the felsite is said to spread out horizontally in places over the truncated edges of the Silurian sediments, but the evidence for this cannot be conclusively demonstrated from present-day exposures. The Silurian strata are exposed on the track for a distance of 200 yd. down the valley. They consist of grey shales and mudstones and have in the past yielded several species of graptolites.

The shape and origin of the Black Hill felsite mass has been a matter for some speculation. Geikie suggested that the felsite forms a vertical sheet intruded along the bedding of the Silurian strata; while Peach described it as a laccolith intruded along the plane of unconformity between the Silurian and Old Red Sandstone sediments. More recently, when it was realized that angular blocks of felsite occur near the base of the overlying conglomerate, that the felsite on the north-west side of Black Hill is locally vesicular, and that certain dyke-like bodies of felsite intrusion-breccia which have a markedly scoriaceous matrix occur within the outcrop, it became necessary to find a theory of origin which could satisfactorily explain all the observed field relationships. One tentative theory suggests that the felsite may have been extruded in early Old Red Sandstone times to form a cumulo-dome, or mamelon, on the Silurian land surface. This dome, it is assumed, was soon covered by greywacke-gravel in which some of the felsite scree forming around the base of the dome was incorporated. The sills and dykes of felsite found in the Lower Old Red Sandstone conglomerate are attributed to a later intrusive phase of activity of the felsite magma.

13. Loganlee: Silurian, Old Red Sandstone Lavas

The Silurian inlier of Loganlee is bounded on the east by a fault with a large easterly down-throw. This is exposed on the north bank of the stream 250 yd. south-west of Loganlee Reservoir, where a layer of purple basaltic tuff, intercalated with lavas of the Carnethy group, abuts against the Silurian.

Along the road to Glencorse Reservoir numerous exposures of this tuff, locally interbedded with ashy sandstone, and of the Carnethy basalt and basic andesite lavas can be examined. A good section of these rocks, including some porphyritic flows of basalt, is also exposed in a southern tributary which enters the Logan Burn at Lovers' Loup, 550 yd. south-west of Loganlee Reservoir.

If this excursion is combined with the Torphin Quarry–Bonally Tower excursion (p. 183), the path leading from Glencorse Reservoir to Bonally Tower should be taken. It is then most convenient to reverse the order of localities in the latter itinerary. Alternatively, good exposures in the rhyolite of Bell's Hill and Castlelaw Hill, and the biotite-dacite of Capelaw Hill, are easily accessible from Glencorse Reservoir. Good sections of auto-brecciated olivine-basalt flows of the Carnethy Group are exposed along the road to Flotterstone.

EXCURSION B

Torphin Quarry—White Hill—Bonally Tower (Route-map p. 184)

Access is by Edinburgh Corporation bus to Torphin (terminus), then ¾-mile walking distance to Torphin Quarry.

1. Torphin: Conglomerates

The road to Torphin Quarry passes to the north of a small escarpment with exposures of pink calcareous conglomerate containing sub-angular pebbles of various Pentland lavas, as well as quartz and quartzite (1). The age of this conglomerate has been taken as Upper Old Red Sandstone, but recently a

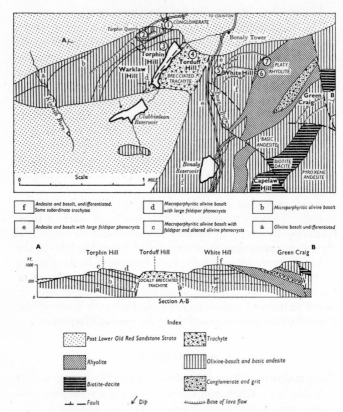

Section A-B

Index

Post Lower Old Red Sandstone Strata

Rhyolite

Biotite-dacite

Fault   Dip

Trachyte

Olivine-basalt and basic andesite

Conglomerate and grit

Base of lava flow

temporary exposure some 400 yd. to the south-east has shown that typical Lower Carboniferous sediments occur very close to the post Lower Old Red Sandstone unconformity in this area. It is therefore quite likely that the Old Red Sandstone is here completely overlapped by the Lower Carboniferous, and that the lavas of Torphin Hill and White Hill may have formed an 'island' till well into Carboniferous times.

2. Torphin Quarry: Basalt Lavas of Lower Old Red Sandstone

The lavas of Torphin Quarry form part of the Warklaw Hill group of olivine-basalts. This is the lowest group in the known portion of the Pentland Hills succession and can itself be divided into four distinctive groups of flows (a–d of route-map). The basalts exposed in the quarry belong mainly to group b, with some flows of group c near the top of the south-east face.

The basalts of group b are black and fine-grained, with small reddish phenocrysts of olivine pseudomorphed by iron oxide and iddingsite. Their groundmass contains much alkaline feldspar and has a trachytic texture. The characteristic feature of the group is the thickness of its two lowest flows. The lowest, which rests on a band of tuff, is up to 60 ft. thick and is locally flow-brecciated near its top. The second flow attains a thickness of nearly 90 ft. and is non-vesicular throughout. The higher flows are much thinner and have weathered tops which pass upward into pebble-beds of weathered lava debris. This suggests that these flows were undergoing rapid weathering and some active erosion shortly after their formation. The flows of group c, which are best examined near the summit of Warklaw Hill, are highly vesicular and are composed of macroporphyritic basalt with phenocrysts of altered olivine and feldspar in roughly equal numbers.

Of the small faults exposed in Torphin Quarry that seen on the east face of the main quarry contains a thin, irregular vein of barytes.

3. Torduff Reservoir: Basalt Lavas of Lower Old Red Sandstone, Glacial features

The highest flows of the Warklaw group (group d) are well exposed on the roadside on the west bank of Torduff Reservoir. They are usually 10 to 12 ft. thick and highly amygdaloidal throughout. The purplish-grey basalts are macroporphyritic, with phenocrysts of altered feldspar measuring up to 5 mm. predominating over the smaller altered ferromagnesian phenocrysts. In the road-cutting 50 yd. south-west of the waterman's cottage a number of veins and irregular masses of siltstone and mudstone are found near the top of a flow; these appear to be filling cracks and cavities in the lava.

Torduff Reservoir lies in the valley formed by a north-east trending fault. In late glacial times this valley formed part of a spillway which marks the final stage in the northward retreat of the ice-sheet from the Pentland Hills.

4. Torduff Hill: Trachyte Lava of Lower Old Red Sandstone

Torduff Hill is formed of pale-grey fine-grained aphanitic trachyte, which closely resembles the trachyte of the Braid Hills near Edinburgh. It is locally flow-banded and there are a number of well-defined belts which have been brecciated in a manner suggesting flow-brecciation. The field evidence suggests that this trachyte is separated from the lava groups on either side by faults, and it seems likely (though not certain) that Torduff Hill forms a structural horst.

5. White Hill: Basalt and Andesite of Lower Old Red Sandstone

The lavas forming the crags of White Hill belong to the Bonally group, which consists of feldspar-phyric olivine-basalts and pyroxene-andesites in its lower part, and of non-porphyritic andesites with one thin flow of trachyte in its upper part. The lower olivine-basalts and andesites are well exposed in the Dean Burn. The upper non-porphyrite flows are seen on White Hill, where they form prominent trap-features, slightly modified by glacial scour.

6 and 7. White Hill Plantation: Rhyolite and Conglomerate of Lower Old Red Sandstone

The Bonally basalts are overlain by the rhyolites of the Bell's Hill and Howden Burn group. On the north-east slope of White Hill a thin conglomerate with pebbles of greywacke, chert and some basic lavas separates these two groups (6). This conglomerate, as well as the overlying rhyolite, can be traced by several outcrops north-eastward downhill through White Hill plantation (7). It can here be demonstrated that the conglomerate rests on the truncated edges of the higher flows of the Bonally group. It is not suggested that a period of earth movement intervened between the eruption of the andesites and the overlying rhyolite: a period of erosion with steep valleys cut into the latest lava flows can be the cause of an angular unconformity of this type.

Return by Bonally Castle to Colinton.

REFERENCES

GEIKIE, A., 1897. *The Ancient Volcanoes of Great Britain*, vol. 1, London, pp. 317-325.

LAMONT, A., 1947. Gala-Tarannon Beds in the Pentland Hills. *Geol. Mag.*, vol. 84, No. 4, pp. 193-208; No. 5, pp. 289-303.

MYKURA, W., 1960. The Lower Old Red Sandstone Igneous Rocks of the Pentland Hills. *Bull. Geol. Surv.*, No. 16, pp. 131-155.

PEACH, B. N., *et al.*, 1910. The Geology of the Neighbourhood of Edinburgh. *Mem. Geol. Surv.*, 2nd edit., pp. 10-41.

PEACH, B. N., 1908. In Cochrane's *Pentland Walks*. 1st edit. (only), pp. 130-150. (See especially pp. 145-147.)

W. MYKURA

CRAMOND-QUEENSFERRY

O.S. One-inch Map, Seventh Series, Sheet 62
G.S. One-inch Map, Sheet 32 (Scotland)
Route-map p. 190

+

INTENDING visitors should note that it is preferable to carry out this excursion when the tide is low. It should also be noted that, by order of the landowner, no cases, bags, or rucksacks may be carried on that part of the coast between the landing-place on the west bank of the Almond at Cramond and Long Craig Gate, about one mile east of Queensferry.

The route described below involves travelling to Cramond by bus or private transport, crossing the River Almond by ferry, walking 5½–6 miles along the coast to Port Edgar, and returning from there by bus or private transport.

The sedimentary rocks to be seen in the course of this excursion belong to the Lower and the Upper Oil-Shale groups of the Lower Carboniferous, the dividing line between the two being taken at the base of the Burdiehouse Limestone. Exposures are discontinuous from Cramond to Peatdraught Bay, but thereafter a fairly continuous section can be seen as far as Port Edgar. Good examples of teschenite and quartz-dolerite sills and their associated contact phenomena can be seen; the teschenite sills are probably of Carboniferous age, and the quartz-dolerite sills probably of Permo-Carboniferous age. Near Queensferry the Pumpherston Oil-Shales and the Pumpherston Shell-Bed are well exposed.

From Cramond to Hound Point most of the exposed strata have a westerly dip, but since these exposures are discontinuous, the structure may be more complex than these dips indicate. Between Whitehouse Point and Port Edgar the rocks form a broad syncline, modified by two relatively small anticlines which underlie the town of Queensferry.

If it is desired to travel to Cramond by bus, a west-bound Corporation (Barnton) bus should be taken. Visitors should alight at Glebe Road, Cramond, walk down Glebe Road, and cross the ferry to the west bank of the River Almond.

1. Cramond Ferry: Teschenite Sill

The ferry jetty on the west bank of the Almond is built on a sill of teschenite (1); the same rock-type forms the large island of Cramond, a mile offshore.

2. Cat's Craig: Teschenite Sill

Another thin sill of the same rock-type, inclined in a westerly direction, forms Cat's Craig (2), 300 yd. along the footpath from the ferry. The feature marking the inner margin of the '25-ft.' raised beach is conspicuous to the left of the path.

3. Hunter's Craig: Sandstone

Hunter's Craig or Eagle Rock, on the shore just over 300 yd. farther on (3), is an outcrop of pale brown sandstone with conspicuous current-bedding. The defaced figure of an eagle on the face of the rock, from which the crag takes one of its names, is supposed to be of Roman origin.

4. Shore between Hunter's Craig and Snab Point: Mudstone and Coal

The strata on the shore immediately west of Eagle Rock include an impure coal seam, 4 in. thick, overlain by mudstone and shale with plant remains and ironstone bands and nodules (4).

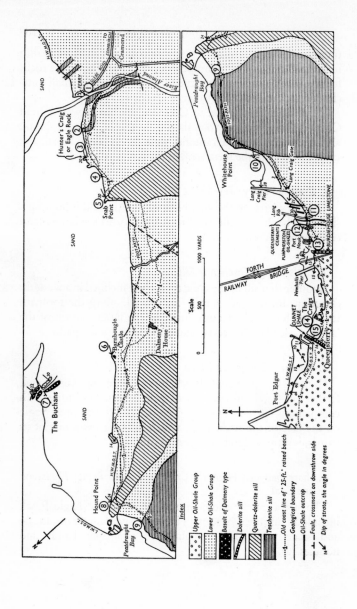

Index

- ⸳°⸳° Upper Oil-Shale Group
- Lower Oil-Shale Group
- ■ Basalt of Dalmeny type
- Dolerite sill
- Quartz-dolerite sill
- Teschenite sill
- ········ Old coast line of '25-ft.' raised beach
- ——— Geological boundary
- ⊥—— Oil-Shale outcrop
- ┄┄┬┄ Fault, crossmark on downthrow side
- ⤩16 Dip of strata, the angle in degrees

Scale

0   500   1000 YARDS

5. Snab Point: Quartz-dolerite Sill

The prominent headland of Snab Point (5) is formed by a sill of quartz-dolerite, inclined to the north-west. The contact between the base of the sill and the underlying shale is exposed on the shore on the east side of the Point, just above high-water mark. The dolerite just above the contact is fine-grained, pale and vesicular; the shale below is dark and indurated, and dips at 30° to the north-west.

6. Barnbougle Castle: Raised Beach

Between Snab Point and Barnbougle Castle (6) there are no exposures of rock on the shore, and it is probable that a fault, trending east-north-east, with a large down-throw to the south, crosses the coast just west of Snab Point. The path between Snab Point and Barnbougle Castle traverses a broad area of raised beach deposits, with some blown sand on the seaward side. The inner margin of the '25-ft.' raised beach deposits is not clearly defined in the region immediately to the south-east of Dalmeny House, but the cliff marking the inner edge of these deposits becomes prominent once again to the north of Dalmeny House.

7. The Buchans: Basalt and Sandstone

It is of interest to note here the group of small reefs known as The Buchans (7), lying about half a mile east of north of Barnbougle Castle; these skerries, which are exposed at low tide, are composed of basalt and sandstone. The basalts, of Dalmeny type, are columnar and vesicular in parts, and probably represent lava flows. The associated sandstones dip at 20°–30° to the west-south-west. A thick bed of sandstone, formerly quarried on the south side of the foot-path, crops out on the shore, half a mile north-west of Barnbougle Castle, the dip being towards the west at about 14°. Between this locality and Hound Point the cliff forming the inner edge of the '25-ft.' raised beach is again prominent.

8. Hound Point: Quartz-dolerite Sill

The promontory of Hound Point is formed by a quartz-dolerite sill, inclined to the south-west; the rock shows columnar jointing in parts. The section to be seen on the shore just east of the Point (8) shows an intercalation of sediment in the sill and is as follows in downward succession: dolerite, fine-grained at base; shale, dark, indurated, with plant remains and fish scales 3 ft.; mudstone, blue-grey, indurated 1 ft.; gap, about 2 ft.; dolerite, blue-grey, fine-grained, with a thin rib of indurated sandstone up to 8 in. thick, 11 ft., on sandstone with indurated top.

The base of the sill cuts into and tilts up the underlying sandstone.

The contact between the top of the sill and the overlying sediments is not exposed, but very fine-grained blue-grey dolerite is seen on the west side of the reef 200 yd. north-west of Hound Point. A good section of blown sand can be seen in the low cliff above high-water mark on the west side of Hound Point.

9. Peatdraught Bay: Teschenite Sill

The next exposure of rock encountered on the shore on the west side of Peatdraught Bay (9) is the lower part of a thick teschenite sill; the sill, the base of which is not seen on the shore, is exposed almost continuously for the next half-mile. Detailed petrographic descriptions of the rock forming this sill have been given by Flett (in Peach et al., 1910) and Walker (1923). The central part of the sill consists of coarse-grained teschenite, while, in the upper and lower parts, there are finer-grained modifications. Walker distinguishes the following modifications, commencing with the lower part, and proceeding upwards: (a) an augite-teschenite, in which most of the titanaugite crystals are idiomorphic; (b) a hornblende-teschenite from which nepheline appears to be absent; there is a sharp, unchilled junction between modifications (a) and

(b); (c) theralite of medium grain, containing small needles of barkevikite; (d) sub-ophitic augite–teschenite; (e) coarse-grained and very coarse-grained augite-teschenite, which forms the bulk of the sill; this central modification contains large ophitic prisms of purplish titanaugite up to half an inch across and six inches long; (f) a more compact sub-ophitic teschenite, with a sharp junction between modifications (e) and (f); (g) theralite, similar to modification (c), with a fairly sharp, unchilled junction with the teschenite below.

10. Whitehouse Bay: Metamorphosed Sediments

The junction between the top of the sill and the overlying sediments is not well exposed, but on the east side of Whitehouse Bay (10), greenish and blue-grey indurated spotted shales and mudstones are seen, dipping west at 13°–19°. Long Craig Pier is built on hard, brown, fine-grained sandstone, dipping westwards at 22°–30°. Along the next 300 yd. of foreshore there are exposures of sandstone, oil-shale and bituminous shale; the shales are rather disturbed and are probably faulted. On the shore, from a point about 320 yd. southwest of the south end of Long Craig Pier to just west of Newhalls Pier there is an almost continuously exposed section of strata belonging to the upper part of the Lower Oil-Shale Group and the lower part of the Upper Oil-Shale Group; the Queensferry Cements, the Pumpherston Shell-Bed, the Pumpherston Shales and the Burdiehouse Limestone, all important horizons, can here be examined.

11. Long Rib: Queensferry Cements and Pumpherston Oil-Shales

The Queensferry Cements, which crop out 360 yd, southwest of Long Craig Pier, and which form the Long Rib, a conspicuous ridge running out to sea, consist of two beds of cementstone. The lower, about 3 ft. 10 in. thick, is brownish-grey in colour, with a yellow-weathering skin, and contains cavities, some of which are filled with bituminous material;

o

Ochil Hills from Stirling showing 'carse', Wallace Monument on Abbey Craig Sill and escarpment of Lower Old Red Sandstone volcanic rocks marking line of Ochil Fault the upper bed, also yellow-weathering, is 1 ft. 2 in. thick, is oolitic, and is separated from the lower by about 3 ft. of grey shale. About 3 ft. 5 in. above the top of the upper cementstone bed there is a thin rib of dark impure limestone (11) containing *Orthoceras*, *Lingula*, lamellibranchs and ostracods, succeeded by soft dark grey shale, 1 ft. 8 in. thick, with numerous *Orthoceras* and ostracods together with occasional shells including a small *Lingula* and lamellibranchs; the fossils are mostly pyritized and the shale has a yellowish efflorescence in the upper part. The last two items represent the Pumpherston Shell-Bed, which has proved of great importance throughout the West Lothian Oil-Shale Field for correlation purposes. It will be noted here that the beds at the top of the low cliff are almost vertical, and that the dip at high-water level is just over 50° to the west.

The strata immediately overlying the shell-bed consist of about 86 ft. of shale and bituminous shale with cementstone and ironstone ribs, and beds of oil-shale representing the Pumpherston Shales. The best band of oil-shale, about 7 ft. thick, is to be found about 18 ft. above the shell-bed, and just to the east of the mouth of a small stream. Features which can be used to identify an oil-shale in the field are as follows: a rich-brown streak; toughness and resistance to weathering; a wooden sound under the hammer; when thin parings are cut from it with a knife, they do not crumble, but curl up. Miners draw a distinction between 'plain' and 'curly' oil-shale; in the former the bedding is regular and in the latter contorted or 'curled'; 'curly' shale usually contains many curved glossy surfaces along which movement has taken place. The contortions in the bedding were probably formed shortly after the deposition of the bed concerned, and before consolidation had occurred.

12. West of Long Rib: 'White Trap'

At the top of the Pumpherston Shales there is a laminated, yellow-weathering, brecciated cementstone, with contorted bedding, and a few feet above is a thin sill of pale decomposed dolerite ('white trap') (12). Many thin dolerite sills which have traversed carbonaceous shales, oil-shales or coals, have been converted into this yellowish or nearly white rock, which consists mainly of carbonates of lime, magnesia, and iron, with kaolin and muscovite. A thin section of white trap, examined between crossed nicols, shows no well-defined structure, but in ordinary light the outlines of the original minerals can be clearly seen. This indicates that these rocks crystallized originally as dolerite, and then, as the temperature fell, were altered by the gases driven from the carbonaceous beds by destructive distillation due to the heat of the dolerite intrusion.

13. Port Neuk: Burdiehouse Limestone, Camps Oil-Shale

A pale dolerite sill, about 2 ft. 3 in. thick, is to be found in the thick sandstone which succeeds the above-mentioned white trap. Part of the Burdiehouse Limestone is exposed just above low-water mark on the west side of Port Neuk (13), the small bay 100 yd. east of the south end of the Forth Railway Bridge. About 3 ft. of dark-grey fine-grained limestone with plant remains and fish remains are seen, overlain by the Camps Oil-Shale. The rocks here are disturbed by a fault, trending north-east, with a down-throw to the north-west. The south end of the Forth Railway Bridge, and Newhalls Pier are built on massive brown sandstones of the Dunnet Sandstone Group, and sandstones of the same group crop out again in the small north-plunging anticline forming the rocks known as The Craigs, 600 yd. west of the south end of the Forth Bridge. The Dunnet Shale is probably present in the small syncline which lies just to the east of The Craigs, but the outcrop of the oil-shale is obscured by superficial deposits.

14. The Craigs: Dolerite Sill

A pale-grey dolerite sill about 2 ft. 6 in. thick crops out on the west side of the anticline at The Craigs (14).

15. Queensferry Harbour: Sill, Oil-Shale and Sandstone

A sill, probably on the same horizon, is seen on the fore-shore just east of Queensferry harbour (15). Here the sill is inclined to the south-east, and is underlain by about 8 ft. of oil-shale and bituminous shale, representing the Dunnet Shale.

Another minor anticline is well seen on the foreshore west of the harbour at Queensferry, where massive sandstones and marly shales and cementstones of the Dunnet Sandstone Group are exposed. The shaly beds in the core of the anticline show good examples of undulating bedding and sun-cracks. Farther west, and immediately east of the east breakwater of Port Edgar, sandstones of this group are again exposed, dipping at a low angle to the north.

The return journey to the outskirts of Edinburgh by Route A.90 traverses strata of the Oil-Shale Group, intruded by sills of teschenite and quartz-dolerite. The solid rocks are mostly obscured by superficial deposits, consisting mainly of boulder clay, but outcrops of teschenite, representing a southward extension of the sill at Whitehouse Point, can be seen by the roadside between one and a quarter and one and three-quarter miles south of east of Queensferry, and the teschenite sill of Corstorphine Hill is exposed on either side of the road, about two miles east of Cramond Bridge.

REFERENCES

CARRUTHERS, R. G., CALDWELL, W., BAILEY. E. M. and CONACHER, H. R. J., 1927. The Oil-Shales of the Lothians. 3rd edit. *Mem. Geol. Surv.*

PEACH, B. N., *et al.*, 1910. The Geology of the Neighbourhood of Edinburgh. 2nd edit. *Mem. Geol. Surv.*

WALKER, F., 1923. The Igneous Geology of the Dalmeny District. *Trans. Roy. Soc. Edin.*, vol. 53, part 2, pp. 361–375.

W. TULLOCH

THE OCHILS from STIRLING

O.S. One-inch Map, Seventh Series, Sheets 54 and 55
G.S. One-inch Map, Sheet 39 (Scotland)
G.S. Six-inch Map, Perth and Clackmannan 133 S.W
Route-map p. 200

THE object of the excursion is to view some of the Lower Old Red Sandstone rocks of the Ochil Hills, starting near Bridge of Allan and ending near Menstrie after descending through a succession of mainly volcanic strata amounting in thickness to some 2000 ft. There are good rail and bus services from Edinburgh to Stirling (37 miles) and from Stirling to Bridge of Allan (3 miles) as well as less frequent through services. From Bridge of Allan the route lies eastwards on foot across country, first ascending to Dumyat (1373 ft.) and then descending to Menstrie through Menstrie Glen. The total walking distance is about 4 miles. There is a frequent bus service back to Stirling (5 miles), but if time is available this journey should be broken at Blairlogie, $1\frac{1}{2}$ miles west of Menstrie, in order to examine minor intrusions and mineralized veins.

The Old Red Sandstone in the ground north of Stirling comprises two subdivisions, the lower of which is volcanic and consists mainly of lavas, tuffs and agglomerates, while the upper is sedimentary and dominantly arenaceous. Between the subdivisions there are transitional strata consisting of coarser sediments derived from erosion of the underlying volcanic rocks and a few intercalated lava flows which appear to represent the final, dying phases of volcanism. All these rocks dip locally to the north-west and the volcanic rocks, more resistant to erosion, form the Ochil Hills while the overlying sediments, in contrast, form the low ground to west and north. The volcanic rocks are cut off to the south by the Ochil Fault beyond which Carboniferous strata lie concealed beneath the flat-lying 'carse' deposits of the low post-glacial raised beach. The fault is a well-known line of instability which has been the source of several minor earthquakes in modern times. At Alva, two miles east of Menstrie, its displacement may be as much as 10,000 ft. and eastward from there, as far as Dollar, the fault is patchily intruded along its plane by quartz-dolerite and is spectacularly exposed along the southern terminations of Alva, Tillicoultry and Dollar glens. From Menstrie to westward the fault is obscured by drift, but the southern slopes of the Ochils form a notable fault-scarp rising steeply from the 'carse'. The volcanic rocks are well-exposed on the scarp-face where the succession can be seen broken by a series of lesser faults which trend to north-north-west.

1. Stirling to Bridge of Allan: Raised Beaches and Quartz-dolerite Sill

The outward route from Stirling to Bridge of Allan traverses the 'carse' of the Forth valley which is here only a mile wide, though to east and west it amounts to 3 miles. The constriction appears to have been caused by a 300-ft. quartz-dolerite sill which is harder than the Limestone Coal Group rocks into which it has been intruded. It forms the eminences of Stirling Castle Rock and the Abbey Craig on the southern and northern sides of the river respectively. From Causewayhead to Bridge of Allan the road runs along a clearly-marked bench feature which backs the low raised beach at a level of about 45 ft. above Ordnance Datum. On the eastern side of the road, in the ground between the Abbey Craig and the Ochil scarp, Airthrey Castle stands on a planed surface of sand and gravel— the deposits of the high late-glacial raised beach—backed by a bench feature at 135 ft. or so above Ordnance Datum.

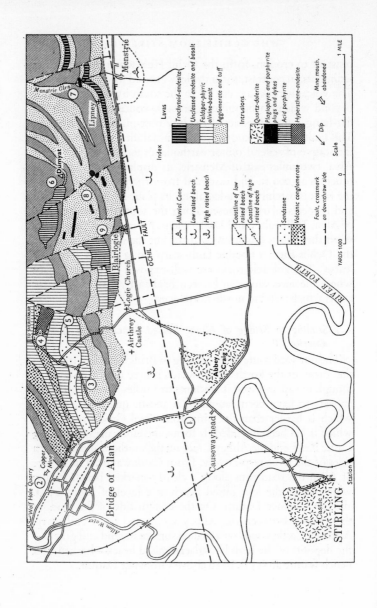

Index

Lavas

Trachytoid-andesite	
Unclassed andesite and basalt	
Feldspar-phyric olivine-basalt	
Agglomerate and tuff	

Intrusions

Quartz-dolerite	
Plagiophyre and porphyrite plugs and dykes	
Acid porphyrite	
Hypersthene-andesite	

Alluvial Cone	
Low raised beach	
High raised beach	

Coastline of low raised beach
Coastline of high raised beach

Sandstone	
Volcanic conglomerate	

Fault, crossmark on downthrow side

Mine mouth, abandoned

Dip

Scale

YARDS 1000   0   1 MILE

STIRLING

RIVER FORTH

Station

Causewayhead

Abbey Craig

Airthrey Castle

Logie Church

Blairlogie

OCHIL FAULT

Bridge of Allan

Allan Water

Wolf Hole Quarry

Copper Mine

Dumyat

Lipney

Menstrie Glen

Menstrie

Castle

2. Wolf Hole Quarry: Lava, Sandstone and Volcanic Conglomerate

Some of the highest transition beds can be examined at Wolf Hole Quarry (790981), on the north-western outskirts of Bridge of Allan. There one of the latest lavas overlies chocolate-coloured, occasionally 'ashy' sandstone from which the fossil fish *Eucephalaspis*, *Pteraspis* and *Scaphaspis* have been collected. East of the quarry volcanic conglomerate, consisting of water-worn pebbles of lava set in a sandy or 'ashy' matrix, crops out in Mine Wood where also an old copper mine can be seen (795979). This was exploited intermittently from 1661 to 1815 and is driven along two veins of pink barytes. The veins, which are still visible in the roof of the mine, contained the copper ores—principally chalcopyrite and 'grey ore' (chalcocite and tetrahedrite)—together with pyrites and mispickel. Bridge of Allan's reputation as a spa was founded on the medicinal properties of the water obtained from this mine. There is a record of an 'Airthrey Silver Mine', discovered in 1761, but its site is not now known.

3. Sheriffmuir Road: Agglomerate and Lavas

From Mine Wood the route lies along the Sheriffmuir road which joins the main Stirling highway a short distance to the south-east of Bridge of Allan (802968). Ascending north-eastwards from this road junction good exposures of agglomerate can be seen in roadside cliffs. Sandstones, some of them tuffaceous, and shales are interbedded with the agglomerates and dip to the north-west or north-north-west at about 10°. The agglomerate is succeeded by feldspar-phyric basalts and an intercalated post of white and purple, partly tuffaceous sandstone.

4. Sheriffmuir Road: Hypersthene-andesite

Near the outcrop of the basalts the stone dykes at the road-side are built of a notable hypersthene-andesite which crops out to the east of the road (815979) approximately three-quarters of a mile north-north-west of Logie Church. As described by Flett (1897) it is a very striking and beautiful rock, pitch black in colour, with a velvety lustre and veins of brilliant red; its great freshness contrasts with the weathered and dull-coloured porphyritic lavas of the neighbourhood. The rock contains no vesicles, but has a well-marked fluxion structure in which phenocrysts of feldspar and green hypersthene are embedded in a mainly glassy groundmass. The rock is mentioned by Geikie (1897, p. 276) under the heading of 'Bedded Lavas', but according to Flett it was mapped by Peach as an intrusive sheet which bakes and hardens the overlying bed of shaly 'ash' and ends abruptly as compared with the more gradual thinning found towards the edges of lavas. At its western end there is, moreover, a suggestion of discordance where the andesite seems to pass down across bedding planes of the adjacent coarse tuff and volcanic conglomerate.

5. North of Logie Church: Basalts and Agglomerates

To the south of the hypersthene-andesite and rising from beneath it there are further exposures of those lavas and coarse pyroclastic rocks already seen at the side of the Sheriffmuir road. The beds of 'ash' were noted by Flett to form little valleys in which they are overlain by a thin coating of boulder clay containing many rocks derived from the districts farther north, while the lavas are sufficiently resistant to erosion to have formed prominent cliffs which can easily be followed running diagonally across the fault-scarp. The topmost lavas are distinctive feldspar-phyric olivine-basalts while those below are pyroxene-andesites. Their vesicles are filled with calcite, chlorite and agate while some flows contain, near the base, baked fragments of shale and sandstone which were evidently caught up during flow. Still lower on the scarp slopes, just above Logie Church, there is exposed a thick band of pink acid porphyrite which is mapped as an intrusion.

6. Dumyat Summit: Intrusion, Lavas and Tuffs

It is not necessary to descend the slopes above Logie Church in order to examine the intrusive acid porphyrite since it is displaced by one of the largest of the north-north-westerly faults and is exposed on both sides of a gully (following the line of another fault) west of the summit of Dumyat (836977). The summit itself is formed by a succession of lavas with thin intercalations of tuff, the lava scarps having been picked out by differential weathering. Traced eastwards down the succession towards Menstrie Glen they give way to a thick band of agglomerate which is interrupted only by a few, thin, impersistent lavas.

7. Menstrie Glen: Lavas

In Menstrie Glen, which consists partly of a deep and inaccessible gorge, the thick band of agglomerate gives way to a thick series of andesitic and basaltic lavas among which Read (1927, p. 89) recognized a dozen separate flows. Two beds of coarse tuff and agglomerate are intercalated near the base of the series: the uppermost is traversed by an east-west dyke which forms a waterfall (848974) across the glen about a quarter of a mile upstream from Menstrie. The lava underlying the tuff is a flow-banded trachytoid-andesite which has a distinctive platy weathering and can easily be traced westward beneath Lipney cottage (846972). Under it there is the lower of the two tuff-and-agglomerate bands already mentioned and this gives way below to some 300 ft. of olivine-basalts. Only the topmost of these appears in the glen at Menstrie, but the whole thickness, in places including agates, is exposed on the hill slopes to the north-east where it is displaced by a group of faults which form prominent gullies parallel to and a short distance to the east of the glen. In places these faults contain stringers of barytes but the mineralization does not compare with that which can be seen above Blairlogie on the return journey to Stirling.

8. Blairlogie: Agglomerates and Minor Intrusions

The steep slopes leading up from Blairlogie to the summit of Dumyat are almost wholly devoid of vegetation and only a few aprons of scree cover the massive agglomerates, altogether about 1000 ft. thick, which crop out there. They form precipitous crags in the faces of which can be seen blocks 'as large as a Highland crofter's cottage' (Geikie 1897, p. 310). Read further says of them: 'although it is inconceivable that these great blocks can have travelled any considerable distance, yet no volcanic vents have been traced anywhere near this end of the Ochils—a circumstance which led Dr Peach to conjecture that the source of these agglomerates must lie buried beneath the Carboniferous sediments to the south, thousands of feet below sea-level.'

The agglomerates are interrupted only by a few thin flows of basalt lava which tail out towards the west. They are traversed also by a few intrusions including some porphyrite dykes, 3 to 10 ft. wide, and by three bosses of plagiophyre which occur close together half a mile or so north-east of Blairlogie. Two of the bosses are adjacent to and on opposite sides of a fault and may together represent a single faulted plug (836972).

9. Blairlogie: Mineralized Veins

The fault last mentioned is the easternmost of the group of north-westerly faults of Blairlogie. The others, on the slopes above the village, are mineralized and have been explored at several points by trial adits, most of which are driven for only a very short distance into the hill. The principal copper ores recorded from these veins are chalcocite and tetrahedrite with some malachite and chrysocolla; there are also traces of lead and silver. The ores are contained in a gangue of mainly pink barytes with impurities in the form of quartz stringers. In places the veins comprise fracture zones containing blocks of lava and tuff strung through with barytes veining. The greatest measured width is 15 ft., exposed about 300 yd. north of Blairlogie (827972) in a small burn which, on its way down the slope to the village, follows the line of the biggest of the group of faults.

REFERENCES

DINHAM, C. H. and HALDANE, D., 1932. The Economic Geology of the Stirling and Clackmannan Coalfield. *Mem. Geol. Surv.*

FLETT, J. S., 1897. A Hypersthene Andesite from Dumyat (Ochils). *Trans. Edin. Geol. Soc.*, vol. 7, pp. 290–297.

GEIKIE, A., 1897. *The Ancient Volcanoes of Great Britain*, vol. i, London.

READ, H. H., 1927. The Western Ochil Hills: *in* The Geology of the District around Edinburgh. *Proc. Geol. Assoc.*, vol. 38, pp. 88–90.

E. H. FRANCIS

BURNTISLAND to KIRKCALDY

O.S. One-inch Map, Seventh Series, Sheets 55 and 56
G.S. One-inch Map, Sheet 40 (Scotland)
G.S. Six-inch Map, Fife 40 N.E.
Route-map p. 208

—

THERE is a frequent train service from Edinburgh to the Fife coast and the following account assumes an outward route by rail to Burntisland and from there along the coast to Kirkcaldy on foot (about 6 miles) and a direct return by rail to Edinburgh. Alternatively one can make the excursion by road or rail to Kinghorn, walk from there along the coast to Seafield and return to Kinghorn by bus.

The rocks between Burntisland and Kirkcaldy belong to the Oil-Shale and Lower Limestone groups. They form part of the north-eastern flank of the Burntisland Anticline—the dominant geological structure in S.E. Fife—and are well-exposed along the shore, where they dip to the east-north-east at 20° to 30°. Many exposures lie below high-water mark and advance reference to tide tables should be made to ensure that the section is seen to best advantage.

Much of the succession consists of basalt lavas which, with subordinate intercalations of tuffs and sediments, amount in thickness to about 1500 ft. The lowest lava is 600 ft. above the Burdiehouse Limestone, which forms the base of the Upper Oil-Shale Group, while the two highest lavas overlie the First Abden Limestone at the base of the Lower Limestone Group. The lavas are olivine-basalts of Dalmeny, Hillhouse and intermediate types but they are not differentiated on the route-map or in the following account. Individual flows are 8 to 40 ft. thick: some show pillow-form; others display columnar jointing: some are vesicular throughout, while others are slaggy only at tops and bases where vesicles are either spheroidal or elongated parallel to the upper and lower surfaces of the lava. The fresher, central parts of the flows vary in coarseness: many pass up into red bole. The tuffs and tuffaceous sediments are normally green, but many of them also pass up into red boles indistinguishable from those at the tops of the lavas. Many of the boles are underlain by patchy semi-lateritized rock which has a fragmental aspect and which is often difficult to identify as either altered tuff or lava.

1. Burntisland and Kingswood

Alight at Burntisland Station where good examples of spheroidal weathering in a dolerite sill are exposed behind the platform; the volcanic vent of The Binn forms a prominent feature behind the town. Take the road leading eastward to Kingswood which runs along the Low (25-ft.) Raised Beach. A mile to the east of Burntisland, on the north side of the coast road, the Kingswood Neck is revealed in a spectacular cliff some 200 yd. long (248865). The neck is formed by grey, coarse massive agglomerate consisting of blocks, up to 3 ft. in diameter, of sedimentary rocks, including limestone and black shale, and earthy and crystalline basalt set in a matrix of fine green basaltic pumice. The western margin of the neck appears to be almost devoid of the coarser blocks. The sedimentary rocks forming the walls of the neck are only poorly exposed on the western side, but to the east sandstones and shales, one of them coaly, are shattered and tilted inwards towards the neck margin. All these features can be seen from the roadside; if closer examination is desired, however, permission should first be sought at the office of the caravan site in the lea of the cliff as this is on private ground; there is also danger from falling stones.

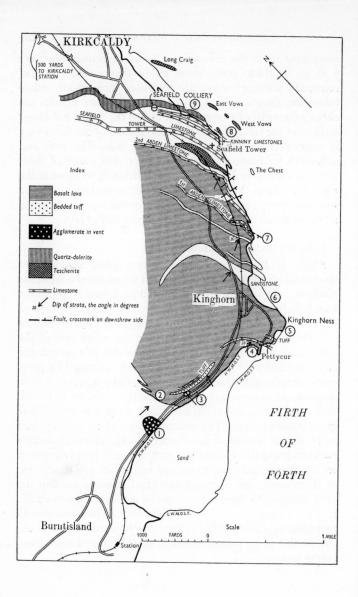

2. Kingswood End: Lavas and Sediments

The lowest of the basalts appears in another cliff on the north side of the road a quarter of a mile east of the last locality. Six flows of lava can be distinguished there; one ranges in thickness from 8 to 40 ft. when traced from east to west. Beds of shale are intercalated with the lavas and near the top of the cliff, above a bed of coarse tuff, the sediments include a limestone which contains plant remains like those of the well-known Pettycur Plant-bed.

3. Kingswood End: Small Neck

Towards the eastern margin of Kingswood End, 60 yd. east of the monument which stands on the south side of the road (255864) a lava overlain by coarse tuff is cut by a dyke-like body of similar coarse tuff, about a foot thick. This contains fragments of indurated sandstone and hades to the west. To the east the lava appears to be somewhat decomposed and within a few feet it is cut off by a mass of unstratified coarse tuff and agglomerate mapped as a small neck only 30 yd. in diameter. The margins of this neck are obscured, but the same basalt lava overlain by coarse tuff reappears in old sand pits farther along the road to Kinghorn.

4. Pettycur: Lavas and Intercalated Sediments

Turning south off the road where it enters Kinghorn, the route continues along the shore starting at Pettycur. Immediately to the east of the pier (266862) a lava is overlain by about 30 ft. of shales with tuffaceous layers and an 18-in. cyprid limestone. These beds are seen best at the side of the road leading to the bottle works where blocks of shale can also be seen caught up in a lava.

5. Pettycur to Kinghorn Ness: Lavas

Walking eastward one traverses an upward succession of lavas dipping in the same direction at 25° to 30°. Thin beds of bole, tuff, tuffaceous sediments and shales occur between some flows. The lowest lava is, in places, breccia-like owing to the large number of inclusions of sediment: some of these were, perhaps, caught up during flow, but the overlying mudstone can be seen adhering to, and filling cracks in, the upper surface of the flow. The third lava from the base, some 200 yd. east of Pettycur Pier, is notably columnar. The columns tend to be hexagonal in cross-section and veins of sediment laced with carbonate traverse the whole flow along certain joints. One of the highest flows, about 30 ft. thick, forms Kinghorn Ness (271861) and can be followed along the coast northward into Kinghorn Bay. It contains rough, scoriaceous masses like coarse agglomerate which led Geikie to regard the flow as a pillow-lava, but which were regarded by D. A. Allan as the result of weathering. The same lava contains abundant xenoliths which are particularly well exposed about 20 yd. south of the southernmost beach shelter (270865). They include well-rounded pebbles of foreign material such as quartzite, jasper, chert and marble, all showing such intense induration that Geikie (1900, p. 69) believed they were 'borne up by the ascending lava-column and were immersed for a long time in a bath of thoroughly liquid rock'.

6. Kinghorn Bay: Sediments

The sandy Kinghorn Bay is hollowed out from relatively soft sandstones which are here about 240 ft. thick though they are known to thin northwards. Very little rock is exposed in the bay, but a hard ganister-like sandstone at the top of the sediments can be seen near the old pier, at the east side of the bay.

7. Kinghorn to Seafield Tower

The ganister-like sandstone is overlain by a 30-ft. lava which is doleritic in texture and vesicular. It is the lowest of a series of flows with partings of sediments, some of them 'ashy'. The highest of these lavas again displays the 'pillow-structure' previously mentioned. It is overlain first by a thin bed of fireclay, then by two beds of dark shale which are separated by 6 ft. of green calcareous tuffs. The lower bed of shale, 4 ft. thick, contains near the base a 1-in. rib rich in fish remains; it comprises the Abden Bone-bed. Marine shells occur above the bone-bed and also in the upper bed of shale which overlies the tuffs. The First Abden Limestone, over-lying the shales, crops out 700 yd. north-north-east of King-horn Pier and its outcrop is broken by a small fault. It is 10 ft. thick and contains corals, crinoids and brachiopods. It is suc-ceeded in turn by 2 ft. of shelly calcareous shales and two basalt lavas separated by a parting of coarse green tuff which passes up into red bole. The lower lava is earthy and has an irregular base containing sedimentary xenoliths; the upper is coarse and doleritic and has red bole at the top. Above the bole a thin bed of pale-grey seatclay is overlain by 8 ft. of dark shales which contain the possibly diagnostic lamellibranch *Naiadites crassus* in a basal 1-in. rib. Pockets of marine shells occur in the upper part of the bed. The Second Abden Lime-stone, 12 to 14 ft. thick, rests on the shales and contains the coral *Lithostrotion junceum* near the base, though it is only sparingly fossiliferous in the upper part. Its outcrop follows the shore northwards for nearly half a mile before passing inland about a quarter of a mile south-west of Seafield Tower. A cave has been formed (278880) along the soft 'crush' of the northernmost of three small, but good examples of dip-faults which dislocate the outcrop.

Between the Second Abden and Seafield Tower limestones there are about 75 ft. of mottled red and grey sediments, mainly sandstones, of which some are strikingly cross-bedded: these sediments are invaded by a teschenite sill, partly trans-gressive, which splits into two leaves as it continues seawards.

8. Seafield Tower (280885): Lower Limestone Group Strata

The Seafield Tower, or Charlestown Main, Limestone crops out immediately south of the ruined Seafield Tower while to

the east the overlying Kinniny Limestones are seen. The following descending succession has been measured there:

		ft.	in.
Upper Kinniny Limestone - - - - - -		1	9
Shales - - - - - - - -		6	0
Strata, obscured - - - - - -		7	0
Shales, shelly at base - - - - - -		9	0
Limestone - - - - -	3 in. to	—	6
Shales - - - - - - -		2	0
Limestone - - - -	1 ft. 9 in. to	4	6
Shales, shelly, especially at top and base - -		40	0
Mid-Kinniny Limestone - - - - -		7	6
Shales - - - - - - -		3	9
Strata, variable, partly obscured - - -		19	0
Sandstone - - - - - - -		11	0
Shales, shelly near base - - - - -		8	8
Strata, obscured, probably shales - - -		7	0
Lower Kinniny Limestone - - - - -		2	3
Shales, top 13 in. coaly - - - - -		1	10
Sandstone - - - - - - -		11	0
Shales - - - - - - -		7	0
Limestone - - - - - - -		—	6
Shales - - - - - - -		8	0
Strata obscured, probably shales - - -		11	0
Limestone - - - - - - -		—	9
Strata, partly obscured, shelly shales at top -		4	9
Coal - - - - - -	up to	3	0
Fireclay - - - - - - -		2	6
Sandstones (*on which the Tower is built*) -		51	0
Shales, shelly - - - - - -		3	6
Limestones, lenticular - - -	up to	3	0
Shales, with limy nodules and lenticular limestone bands - - - - - - -		38	6
Seafield Tower Limestone - - - -		10	6

The 3-ft. coal of this section is usually obscured by beach sand, but the Kinniny limestones are exposed along the shore to the north-north-west as far as Seafield Colliery and in this stretch some small-scale thrusting can be seen in the Mid-Kinniny Limestone and adjacent beds.

9. Seafield Colliery (277894): Limestone Coal Group Strata

A transgressive sill of quartz-dolerite, which occurs among the Kinniny limestones in the Seafield shafts, overlies the Upper Kinniny Limestone on the shore to the south-east. Above it there are the fine- and coarse-grained sandstones with intercalations of shales and ironstones which comprise the lower part of the Limestone Coal Group. The off-shore skerries of Long Craig, East Vows and West Vows are formed by a teschenite sill intruded higher in the same group.

REFERENCES

ALLAN, D. A., 1924. The Igneous Geology of the Burntisland District. *Trans. Roy. Soc. Edin.*, vol. 53, pp. 479–501.

ALLAN, J. K. and KNOX, J., 1934. The Economic Geology of the Fife Coalfields, Area II. *Mem. Geol. Surv.*

GEIKIE, A., 1900. The Geology of Central and Western Fife and Kinross-shire. *Mem. Geol. Surv.*

GORDON, W. T., 1914. The Country between Burntisland and Kirkcaldy: *in* The Geology of the District around Edinburgh, 2nd edit. *Proc. Geol. Assoc.*, vol. 25, pp. 34–40.

E. H. FRANCIS

ELIE to ST MONANCE

O.S. One-inch Map, Seventh Series, Sheet 56
G.S. One-inch Map, Sheet 41 (Scotland)
Route-map p. 216

Route-map p. 216

THE excursion is designed to start at Elie, which can be reached by train from Edinburgh, thence walking the rocky coast section (3 to 4 miles) to St Monance and returning to Edinburgh by train. Advance reference should be made to tide tables since most of the exposures lie below high-water mark.

Along this coast a series of necks breaks through the Lower Carboniferous sedimentary rocks and 'furnish an unrivalled body of material for the study of . . . the structure of volcanoes' (Geikie 1902, p. 200). The necks are filled with fragments of the surrounding strata, brought up from no great depth; they include coal, sandstone, shale, limestone and ironstone and range in size from particles of dust to blocks several yards long. There is, in addition, a varying proportion of basalt in the form of both small, pale lapilli and large crystalline and vesicular blocks. Dykes and veins of basalt and fine-grained tuff traverse the necks and also the adjacent strata which are usually fractured and tilted in towards the neck margins.

The ground is traversed by the Ardross Fault, a tear-fault calculated by Cumming (1936, p. 351) to have a dextral horizontal movement amounting to 4000 ft.; this figure is obtained by matching the Elie Ness Neck with the Ardross Neck and the Wadeslea Neck with the Coalyard Hill Neck. The sedimentary rocks are tightly folded against the fault and the complete succession has yet to be made out. There are, however, four recognizable limestones which are named, in upward succession, the Lower Ardross, Upper Ardross, St Monance White and Wood Haven limestones. The Lower Ardross Limestone is correlated with the First Abden, or Charlestown Station Limestone of other parts of Fife; this is currently taken to form the base of the Limestone Coal Group and is equated with the Hurlet Limestone of the Central Coalfield, though Geikie and Cumming use the name 'Hurlet' when referring to the St Monance White Limestone.

1. Elie Harbour Neck

The neck at the end of the harbour at Elie (492996) is formed by dark tuff and agglomerate the larger fragments of which, up to 3 ft. in diameter, are of crystalline and slaggy basalt; the vesicles in some are arranged concentrically. At the west side of the neck there is a mass of hardened sandstone and shale measuring 10 ft. by 12 ft. The neck is traversed by several small faults, by a few narrow, sinuous dykes of basalt and by veins of fine-grained tuff and calcite. The tuff and agglomerate at the western and southern parts of the neck are well-bedded and dip inward towards the centre of the neck at angles as high as 65°. The margins of the neck lie beyond low-water mark to west and south, but to the north the agglomerate encloses a large, shattered mass of nearly vertical white and red false-bedded sandstones with shales and a thin coal seam. One of the sandstones is very coarse and contains pebbles of opaline quartz and grains of almandine garnet, the latter in such quantity as to lend a pink colour to the rock. The mass is permeated by fine-grained tuff continuous with the main neck filling and it is traversed by a basalt dyke. The eastern wall of the vent is formed by hardened sandstone dipping inwards at angles approaching vertical. This dip decreases away from the neck and the sandstones pass down into shales overlying the Wood Haven Limestone which is $3\frac{1}{2}$ to 5 ft. thick. Small-scale

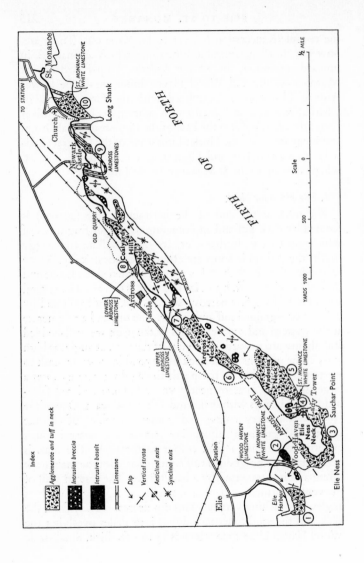

Index

Agglomerate and tuff in neck

Intrusion breccia

Intrusive basalt

Limestone

Dip

Vertical strata

Anticlinal axis

Synclinal axis

FIRTH OF FORTH

St. Monance

ST. MONANCE WHITE LIMESTONE

Long Shank

TO STATION

Church

Newark Castle

ARDROSS LIMESTONES

OLD QUARRY

Coalyard Hill

W. ARDROSS

N. ARDROSS NECK

Ardross Castle

LOWER ARDROSS LIMESTONE

UPPER ARDROSS LIMESTONE

Station

Elie

WOOD HAVEN LIMESTONE

ST. MONANCE WHITE LIMESTONE

Wood Haven Neck

Elie Ness

S. ARDROSS HILL

Ardross Neck

WEST NECK

ST. MONANCE WHITE LIMESTONE

Lady Tower

Sauchar Point

Elie Harbour

Elie Ness

Scale

YARDS 1000   500   0   ½ MILE

dip-faulting is apparent in the shift of these beds and they are traversed by dykes of white trap. They also contain, 100 yd. east of the neck (495996), an intrusion breccia which is pear-shaped in ground-plan and consists entirely of shattered sedimentary rock.

2. Wood Haven Bay: Basalt (?boss) with Tuff Veins

Following the Wood Haven Limestone northward into the sandy bay between Elie Harbour and Elie Ness a mass of intrusive basalt is reached (496997). It has a wide marginal zone of white trap and displays a network of veins, up to 6 in. thick, of carbonate and fine tuff: some of the tuff is grey and apparently devoid of basaltic debris. Since some of the veins close upwards they are likely to be intrusive. Immediately to the west of the western margin of the basalt, and at a somewhat lower horizon than the Wood Haven Limestone, the St Monance White Limestone is partially exposed.

3. Elie Ness Neck

Continuing around Wood Haven Bay towards Elie Ness the northern margin of the Elie Ness Neck with beach sand is straight-edged and probably marks the approximate position of the Ardross Fault. The neck itself consists of dull, dark-green stratified tuffs and agglomerates containing blocks of basalt and sedimentary rocks and crystals of orthoclase, hornblende and pyroxene; the last two form aggregates in irregular lumps up to 4 or 5 in. in diameter. Pyrope garnet (Elie ruby) is also a well-known constituent, but it does not occur uniformly throughout the neck.

Near the south-western headland, about 30 yd. west of the lighthouse (496993) there is a boss of basaltic agglomerate, about 20 yd. in diameter, which stands above the bedded tuffs and agglomerates. Veins of fine tuff and carbonate, up to 1 ft. thick, traverse the boss and the rocks beyond it and the fine-grained tuff can be seen in places to be 'stratified' parallel to the walls of the veins, suggesting that they are intrusive in origin. Another boss of coarse, basaltic agglomerate stands out at Sauchar Point (499993), at the south-eastern extremity of the neck. In the intervening ground the tuffs and agglomerates dip inwards and form striking scarp featuring; hereabouts, too, they contain a higher proportion of sedimentary-rock debris, including white-weathering limestones. Still farther east towards the margin of the neck, the number of tuff veins increases and basalt dykes appear. One of the latter, just east of the Lady's Tower (500995), terminates downwards and has hardened the surrounding tuffs to form a line of prominent stacks. The eastern margin of the neck is exposed just east of the Lady's Tower where its ground-plan has a serrated line. The agglomerate here is crowded with blocks of the adjacent strata and is, in places, darkened by included shale or made yellow by included sandstone. The sedimentary rocks outside the vent are indurated and bent inwards at angles approaching vertical in some places; in other places the wall-rocks are intimately penetrated by the neck material and the margin is there difficult to delineate.

4. Elie Ness and Wadeslea: Intrusion Breccias

In the bay east of the Lady's Tower there is a stretch, 100 to 200 yd. wide, occupied by sedimentary rocks. These are folded anticlinally against the north-eastern margin of the Elie Ness Neck and dip eastward towards the Wadeslea Neck. Two dykes of white trap traverse the sediments and several bodies of breccia are exposed. The breccias consist almost entirely of sedimentary rock apparently broken in places and only slightly deranged: some blocks of sandstone are as much as 9 ft. across. The matrix is formed by a dark-grey tuff, wholly derived from sediments in some places but partially basaltic in others. The margins of the breccias are poorly defined; they pass laterally, in places, into the surrounding undisturbed strata. One body is intruded along the plane of a small fault which lies close to and parallel to the western margin of the Wadeslea Neck.

5. Wadeslea Neck

The agglomerate of the Wadeslea Neck has a pale green basaltic matrix, but contrasts with the Elie Ness and Ardross necks since it contains a much higher proportion of sedimentary rock among the larger bombs. These are mainly derived from the adjacent strata with which, in places, the inclusions coincide both in dip and strike. They give the impression that during the volcanic process the strata have been absorbed into the neck and this impression is enhanced by exposures at the western margin (501996) which show the neck material intruded into the sediments. The St Monance White Limestone forms the south-western margin of the neck at low-water mark. Farther east, also near low-water mark, there is a boss of black basaltic agglomerate resembling those in the Elie Ness Neck.

6. Ardross Fault

The northernmost exposures of the Wadeslea Neck are separated from the southern by a boulder beach. Where it first appears the Ardross Fault forms a gully about 4 ft. wide (503001). There is a marked contrast between the agglomerates on either side, the larger fragments in the Wadeslea Neck being mainly sedimentary while those in the Ardross Neck are almost entirely basaltic. Tracing the fault to the north-east the Ardross agglomerate continues in juxtaposition, but the Wadeslea agglomerate gives way to sandstones containing intrusion breccias like those seen farther west.

7. Ardross Neck: Eastern Margin

The Ardross agglomerate continues beneath a sandy bay and reappears to the north-east where it is traversed by coarse basalt dykes trending north-west and forming high walls above the beach (506004). At the vent margin hereabouts the agglomerate and the adjacent, vertically inclined sediments are laced with calcite veinlets also vertically aligned. A yellow limestone—the St Monance White—dips into the plane of the Ardross Fault where it intersects the neck margin and farther north large blocks of the same limestone, up to 10 ft. long, are caught up just inside the neck. The sandstones close by are fractured and contain a network of thin veins of tuff.

South of the ruins of Ardross Castle (508007), between the Ardross and Coalyard Hill necks, the sediments, including the prominent Upper Ardross Limestone, are broken and shifted by small-scale faulting. The Ardross Fault can be followed across the strata and near the place where it cuts off the outcrop of the Upper Ardross Limestone another intrusion breccia may be examined.

8. Coalyard Hill Neck

Approaching the Coalyard Hill neck from the south-west the neck margin can be seen forming a buttress which stands about 3 ft. higher than the adjacent anticlinally folded sediments. The margin follows a sinuous course to the north-east and the agglomerate, crowded with sedimentary blocks, 'tongues' into the recesses of the adjacent strata. Just below the railway embankment (511008) the Lower Ardross Limestone crops out against a small basalt intrusion marginal to the main agglomerate. Here also, in the agglomerate, there is a high incidence of calcite veining parallel to the vent margin. A short distance to the south-west the Ardross Fault cuts off the agglomerate and for about 180 yd. of its length it encloses a detached, lenticular mass of sandstone and shale about 20 yd. wide. Near the fault a large mass of basalt capping agglomerate forms a prominent stack (513008).

The sediments to the south-east of the Ardross Fault and opposite the Coalyard Hill Neck are tightly folded and faulted. They include, about 600 yd. east-north-east of Ardross

Farm, a small neck (515009) elongated eastward and terminating there with a knob of basalt. North of it, re-crossing the Ardross Fault and yet another intrusion breccia, the sedimentary rocks are well exposed to the north-east of the Coalyard Hill Neck where folding and faulting can be studied in detail on the beach and along the face of an old quarry (515011).

9. Newark Castle: Necks, Faulting and Folding

The Newark Castle Neck is met 200 yd. or so north-east of the old quarry; it consists of dull–green agglomerate with quartz grains in the matrix. The western margin is vertical against sandstone which is fractured and injected by fine tuff. At a point 150 yd. west of Newark Castle the agglomerate ends against the Ardross Fault which here leaves the coast. The strata to the south-east of the fault are tightly folded and include, a short distance to the west of the castle, an intrusion breccia which is traversed by a basalt dyke. Beneath the castle (518012) the Ardross limestones and adjacent strata are well exposed, dipping eastwards at a high angle to form the western limb of a syncline. The overlying white, false-bedded sandstone, on which the castle is built, occupies the centre of the syncline and the limestones reappear in the bay farther east where they are arched into an anticline. This structure is broken, 100 yd. east of the castle, by a small but particularly well-exposed neck—the Dovecot Neck (520012)—formed by agglomerate containing sedimentary blocks, one of which consists of indurated sandstone and measures 7 yd. by 24 yd. The blocks are set in a matrix of green tuff which penetrates the disturbed strata adjacent to the neck margin.

10. St Monance Neck

At the east end of the bay the sandstone overlying the Ardross limestones dips eastward and forms a high wall extending seaward to form Long Shank (522011). The wall is breached near high-water mark by a basalt dyke which has proved less resistant to erosion than the sandstone and is now marked by a gap. The dyke continues eastwards into the body of the St Monance Neck which is exposed on the shore below St Monance Church (523014). The neck consists of unstratified agglomerate containing blocks which are mainly basaltic except near the western margin where a high proportion of sandstone appears. At this margin, too, the tuff and agglomerate of the neck are seen to be locally intrusive into the sandstone forming the wall-rock. The neck is traversed by several basalt dykes some of which stand up above the beach while others have weathered into narrow depressions; they are particularly well displayed at the western margin. Beyond the eastern margin, which is partly obscured, sandstones dipping eastward are succeeded by the St Monance White Limestone.

REFERENCES

CUMMING, G. A., 1928. The Lower Limestones and Associated Volcanic Rocks of a Section of the Fifeshire Coast. *Trans. Edin. Geol. Soc.*, vol. 12, pp. 124–140.

——1936. The Structural and Volcanic Geology of the Elie-St Monance District, Fife. *Trans. Edin. Geol. Soc.*, vol. 13, pp. 340–365.

GEIKIE, A., 1902. The Geology of Eastern Fife. *Mem. Geol. Surv*.

WALLACE, I. F., 1916. Notes on the Petrology of the Agglomerates and Hypabyssal Intrusions between Largo and St Monans. *Trans. Edin. Geol. Soc.*, vol. 10, pp. 348–362.

W. E. H. FRANCIS

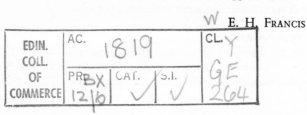